ELECTRICS

D1555944

Roy Bacon

OSPREY

Published in 1988 by
Osprey Publishing Limited,
27A Floral Street, London WC2E 9DP
Member company of the
George Philip Group

British Library Cataloguing in
Publication Data

Bacon, Roy H. (Roy Hunt)
   Restoring motorcycle electrics
   1. Motorcycles. Electrical systems.
   Maintenance & repair. Amateurs'
   manuals
   I. Title
   629.2'54
ISBN 0-85045-788-2

Editor Tony Thacker
Design Gwyn Lewis

Filmset and printed by
BAS Printers Limited,
Over Wallop, Hampshire,
Great Britain

PAGE 1 Electrics of the early days were often extras, as with these lighting sets, batteries and horn sold for the owner to add to his machine

FRONT COVER/PAGE 3 The electrics of a 350 cc B31 BSA of 1949 vintage

Contents

The massive Ducati Apollo V4 engine, with a
distributor on each end of a cross-shaft fed by
undertank coils

Acknowledgements

This is the second book in a new series designed to assist and guide motorcycle restorers in the techniques and tricks they need when working on their machines. In these areas, it goes into more detail than a marque restoration book and is concerned with what to do and how to do it.

In its preparation, I have to thank Ken Hallworth of *Old Bike Mart* and Bryan Simmons of Biggin Hill for their help in reading the manuscript, correcting my errors and adding items I had missed. The legal section went under the sharp eye of Dr Bickerstaff, and between us we tried to unravel the legal needs of the rider in the UK, which was harder than it ought to be. All the assistance was most appreciated.

Many of the photographs used were specially commissioned for the book and taken by Chris Nicoll with the help of Bryan Simmons who provided samples of parts, repair work methods and test equipment, while others came from Boyer Bransden Electronics, Mistral Engineering and Piranha. Once again the magazines were a great help and I have to thank the EMAP archives which hold the old *Motor Cycle Weekly* files and Malcolm Gough of *Motor Cycle News* for their assistance.

A good number of line drawings were used to illustrate the text as these often show detail needed better than a photograph. These came from many sources, some from way back in the mists of the past. Known sources were BSA, BTH, Champion, Lucas, Miller, Norton, Royal Enfield, Siba, Triumph, Villiers and Wipac, as far as can be determined.

Some of the photographs used carried the imprint of a professional, and the ones used came from Andrew Morland, Bruce Main-Smith, Dave Minton, and B.B. Commercial Studios Ltd. As usual, all those borrowed were returned to their files after publication and I have tried to make contact to clear copyright. If my letter failed to reach you or I have used an unmarked print without realizing this, please accept my apologies.

Finally, my thanks to all at Osprey who helped turn this concept into its final form.

Roy Bacon
Niton, Isle of Wight
March 1988

Introduction

The electrics of a motorcycle tend to frighten restorers, but there is no need for this. Just as with all the other jobs, you have to arm yourself with tools and data. This book sets out to give you the latter and advise you on what is needed for the former.

The chapters cover the systems fitted to two- and four-strokes, with the emphasis on post-war British machines as this is the area most restorers will be involved in. However, the pre-war period is not neglected and some of the strange devices of the 1920s are touched on.

The aim of this book is to assist and guide the reader in his or her work on motorcycle electrics. It is hoped that the result will be fine sparks and bright lights, and every endeavour had been made to offer helpful and safe advice.

However, the onus is always with the reader to ensure that anything he or she works on or uses in a complete machine is in good order. Also, all work should be carried out in a sensible manner with due regard to safety precautions.

Neither the author nor the publisher can accept any liability for anything contained in this book which may result in loss, damage or injury, and the book is only available for purchase or loan on that basis.

So, if you zap yourself with the ignition, fry the battery or pop your zener, it is your fault and nothing to do with me or us!

You have been warned—be sure to check your work before starting up or connecting the power.

This forward battery mounting was used by Douglas for several models in the 1930s, while the magneto was mounted in this style on top of the crankcase for many years

CHAPTER 1
Basic tools and techniques

Motorcycle electrics worry most owners more than anything else on their machine, one of the reasons being that you never see the electrical flow, only its effects. The difficulty is that, like an oil leak, electrical problems can spread all over the place with little indication of where they originated.

To restore a system and its parts, you have to get to grips with it. Once this is done, many of the difficulties fade away. Just as with mechanical items, you need to know how the electrics work, and have the tools for working on the parts and the setting data to get them operating as they should. This is mainly different rather than difficult, but often calls for more thought because you cannot see what is happening or where the power flows.

Fortunately, believe it or not, most problems are due to mechanical faults rather than electrical ones, and so are not as hard to deal with. Electronic circuits and encapsulated units are another matter, however, and are usually sealed and impossible to mend. These should be replaced if faulty, but are not very common on the machines most people restore. It *is* possible to dig into a unit sealed with compound, but it can take a long time and you have to be careful how you do it. I once did this with a CDI box but it took a week to get to the circuit and components!

Some basics

The electrical system of most machines has a battery at its heart to act as a store from which the various services draw their supplies to feed the ignition, lights, horn and other items. To refill the store, there is a generating system which may be a dynamo or an alternator, though the operating basis remains the same in principle.

Various analogies can be made, such as a water tank being filled and drawn from, but essentially the battery is charged up by the generator and drained by everything else. Complication tends to arise in controlling the generator to match the needs of the battery and its system, but even this is now much easier thanks to the wonders of modern electronic components.

In addition to the battery system, there are

The simplest system of all was the flywheel magneto with direct lighting that went out when the engine stopped

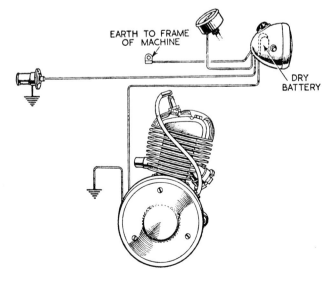

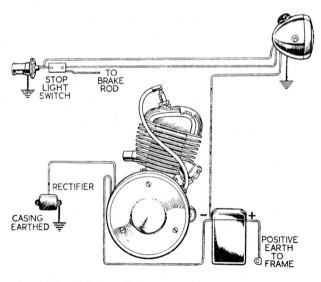

STOP
LIGHT
SWITCH

TO
BRAKE
ROD

RECTIFIER

CASING
EARTHED

POSITIVE
EARTH
TO
FRAME

The addition of a battery and rectifier gave a reserve and the chance to add a stop light and horn to the system

other types, the most common of which is the direct-lighting method used on many two-stroke machines. These have a flywheel magneto on the crankshaft providing the ignition and current for the lights, which only work while the engine is running. The system has technical and legal problems, but was always cheap to install and easy to wire up.

Some machines, however, dispense with lights altogether and may rely on magneto, energy transfer or electronic means for their ignition. All of these systems may be combined with battery lights and frequently are.

Amps, ohms, watts and volts

These are the units by which electricity is measured, and an understanding of them helps in just the same way as a circle and degrees help with valve timing and inches with measurement. Again, the water analogy is usually given and works for most people.

A volt is the unit of electromotive force that pushes the electricity along the wires—more volts means more push, which helps the flow. This is slowed down by the resistance, which is measured in ohms. As you might expect, a long, thin wire offers more resistance than a short, thick wire, hence the use of heavy cables to power starter motors which need lots of flow.

The rate at which the electricity flows, or its current, is expressed in amperes, usually

shortened to amps, while the unit of power is the watt. Again, as expected, the flow is slower along thin wires with a low voltage, and the resulting amount of power is small. However, reducing the resistance and increasing the voltage will put up the flow rate and hence the amount of power or number of watts.

The four units relate to one another in two formulae. One states that volts equals amps multiplied by the resistance, and the other states that watts equals volts multiplied by amps. By combining them, watts also equals resistance multiplied by the current squared. These are worth noting as they can help in deciding the battery size and whether extra lamps can be installed to the system. An example is a 30-watt headlight bulb on a 6-volt system, which will take 5 amps of current to power it. The 6-watt tail bulb would take another amp, while the stop light, when used, would impose a further 21 watts on the system.

The battery capacity is given in ampere-hours and as a ten-hour rate in most cases. This is because a heavy demand on the battery will not only flatten it more quickly but will accelerate this. Thus a 12-ampere-hour battery will give 1.2 amps for the ten hours but not 2.4 amps for five hours. It certainly would not give 12 amps for one hour or anything like it.

Currents and magnets

The battery used on a motorcycle can be recharged as it is a secondary cell. Like all batteries, it supplies direct current and has two terminals, with the electricity flowing from the positive terminal to the negative one. In early days, the convention was to earth the negative terminal, but this changed in the early 1950s to positive earth, and again in the 1970s back to negative. You must connect the battery the right way round, but the earth remains simply a common return line using the machine frame in place of or in addition to the wires.

The circuit flow is thus always in the one direction and dynamos produce current in this form—but not alternators or flywheel magnetos. For these an external rectifier is used to turn their alternating current into direct current, or ac to dc. In either case, the current is generated by moving electric wires relative to a magnetic field. The field can come from a permanent magnet or one formed by passing a current through a wire. It does not take very much

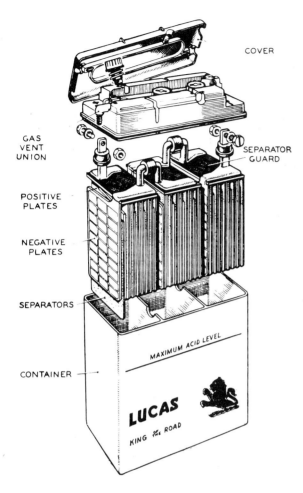

GAS
VENT
UNION

COVER

POSITIVE
PLATES

NEGATIVE
PLATES

SEPARATOR
GUARD

SEPARATORS

MAXIMUM ACID LEVEL

CONTAINER

LUCAS
KING of the ROAD

Typical 6-volt battery construction, with each cell producing 2 volts and the three joined in series

current to do this, so once it is under way a little of the generated current can be used for this purpose.

Either the wire or the field can be moved to provide the current, and in practice there are many wires and several magnets. They are arranged so that one part can be driven by the engine and, thanks to this rotation, will thus produce an alternating current. This is turned into the desired direct current inside the dynamo by the commutator and externally by a rectifier for the alternator.

Diagram troubles

These give most of us a good deal of trouble as few are laid out in a helpful manner. Part of the difficulty arises in the way the original factory drawing is shrunk to fit into the instruction manual, thus becoming too small to read,

but there are other problems also. Most arise from the layout and the lack of switch data.

Diagrams are laid out as a plan view of the machine in many cases, or simply as the parts come in others. Often the wiring is shown as a group of parallel lines, and following these in order to choose the correct turn-off is seldom easy. Further complication comes from the differences between this working diagram and a true theoretical circuit diagram.

This theoretical circuit diagram often forms the basis of other diagrams used to illustrate working principles, and it invariably ignores the physical distances between components and the wiring joints and connections between them. Often, these wires will have other lines running from them, leading to even more confusion.

The final obstacle in the path of linking theory, practice and the hardware comes at the switches. All too often the diagram simply says 'light switch' and shows terminals and the wires attached to them, but without showing the internal connections at each switch position. This information, though, is vital to understanding the way in which the circuit connects up and functions.

However, if all this is clarified and put together, it then becomes much easier to work out the charging circuit and what happens at each stage. The lights and ignition services are generally easier—though not always, as they may be involved in the control of the charging circuit.

A diagram that you have worked out and drawn yourself will always be the simplest to understand, so be sure to do this as the time will be well spent and the result a great help.

Information

Some of what you need is contained in these pages, but reference should be made to the wiring diagram for your machine, amplified to be helpful as above, plus the data on individual parts of the system.

The points gap of a magneto, voltage setting of a regulator or current drain of a horn can be just as important as the engine valve clearance or rear-chain free play to the machine's well-being and your riding enjoyment. Most problems can be cured by cleaning parts and connections, followed by correct adjustment of the settings.

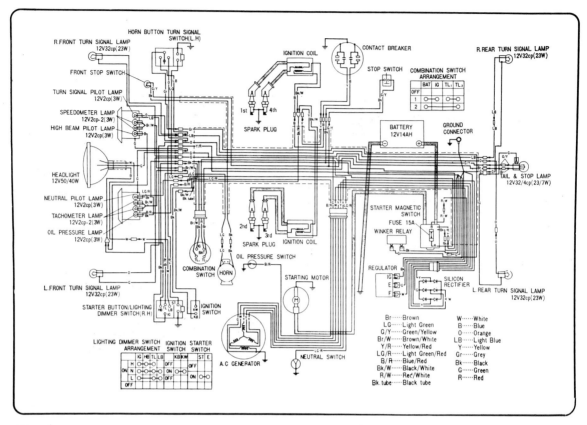

Typical wiring diagram which becomes impossible to read in many manuals

Tools

Most electrical parts are smaller and lighter than those of the engine and gearbox, and it is important that your tools for working on them should reflect this. The work is also generally cleaner, so the tools need to be kept free from dirt—some may even be best kept for this work alone, and for the carburettor jobs which have similar needs.

Spanners must fit. Self-evident though this may seem, it matters far more with small nuts than large. It is feasible, although bad practice, to use a 23 mm spanner on a $\frac{7}{8}$ in. nut, but if you try to turn a 2BA nut with a $\frac{3}{8}$ in. spanner, it will just run round. Electrical assemblies often have odd nut sizes, so ideally you will need a set of spanners ranging from oBA to 8BA for British machines, $\frac{3}{16}$ in. to $\frac{7}{16}$ in. for American or Unified threads, and 4 mm to 11 mm for Europeans. Both open-ended spanners and $\frac{1}{4}$ in. drive sockets are commonly used and many restorers use nut runners of the type to be found in the electronics industry.

Screwdrivers need to fit the screws, so you may require basic blades and Philips or Pozidrive tips. Be wary of interchangeable kits as some are of poor quality and it can be a bind

having to change the driver bit too often. Magnetic and head grip drivers can be useful in some places, but for most assemblies a set of good-quality screwdrivers will be the best things to have. (These will benefit from being used only on the electrics and not for levering a gearbox into place.)

For small screws, a set of jeweller's screwdrivers with rotating tops is most useful. They allow one finger to hold the tool in place while the thumb and another finger turn it.

Only use quality tools. Nowhere is this more important than with wire cutters. These come in all shapes and sizes, but a 6 in. side cutter will cover most needs, while a light, thin 4 in. cutter is useful for dealing with odd stray wires. Before buying any cutter, hold it up to the light and check how well the cutter edges come together. Don't be afraid to run through the box to get a decent tool as there are plenty that are not satisfactory.

The same applies to pliers and there are even more of these. One with long jaws, one with

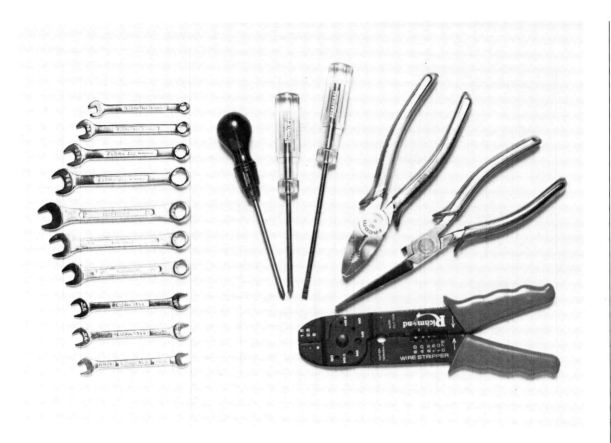

Neat set of the kind of tools you need for electrical work, which are best kept for this use alone

round and one a little heavier will be quite sufficient for your needs. Forget the rest of your collection except for odd, special jobs where their careful use may pay. You may need circlip pliers which must have tips that fit securely into the clips without slipping out in use, but these are best bought as required.

Similar to pliers are tweezers—electronic or instrument fitters always have various pairs of these. They allow you to pick up small nuts and washers easily and then fit them in places that are unreachable with your fingers—very handy at times.

Wire strippers come in many forms, though few will remove the insulation without nicking the wire beneath it. All claim to leave the wire clean but very few do. When buying, take various gauges of wire with you and try the tool on all of them. Select the best and use it with care—that way, you will not damage the wire too badly.

You may use crimping tools on the wiring. Both these tools and the parts they work on must match, as a poor joint can easily occur and cause endless trouble. If this happens it can be a trial to locate the problem area, especially if it gives intermittent contact. Some crimp

joints are done using pliers and are intended to add on wires rather than produce a harness.

Older machines tend to have their terminals soldered in place, thus an iron will be needed. Something in the order of 50 watts should be about right for wiring and general-purpose soldering but not for electronics. If you get involved in this area, something much smaller with a fine tip would be better.

If you solder electronic components you may need a heat sink. This is a means of preventing too much heat pouring into an item that would wilt under the strain. Many technicians use a small crocodile clip with a block of brass soldered to it as this provides both a heat sink and a means of attachment. They are clipped to the component lead between the electronic part and the iron. Whether you crimp or solder, always work to the highest standard.

Finally, there are the instruments you will use. The most important will be a good-quality multi-meter, with either a scale and pointer or digital read-out. Don't buy a very cheap one

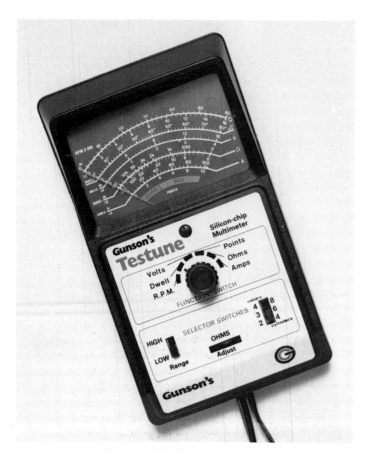

as this may only be good enough for continuity checks—you need something a little better, even if not of laboratory quality. Do aim for the meter to have the ranges that you will need.

You are likely to want scales that read 0–20 volts, 0–30 amps, and 0–500 ohms, plus ones for mains voltage, milli-amps and thousands of ohms. An old ammeter from a machine can also be useful as it will have a centre zero and read to 12 or 15 amps either way. Equip it with leads with clips on their ends.

A hydrometer for testing the specific gravity of the battery is well worth having, as is a decent battery charger. This should be able to deal with 6- and 12-volt batteries, and if it has a means of varying its output, so much the better.

A handy test item is a bulb with leads soldered to it. If one lead is attached to earth, the other can be used to check which terminals are live or not. It can also be used across points when setting ignition timing. A variation on this is a torch modified to have two leads with probes attached, which allows circuit tests without involving the machine battery. This can be handy when trouble strikes during a journey.

ABOVE **Small meter designed for car engine use and handy for two wheels as well**

BELOW **The hydrometer used to test the battery's specific gravity and essential for monitoring its health**

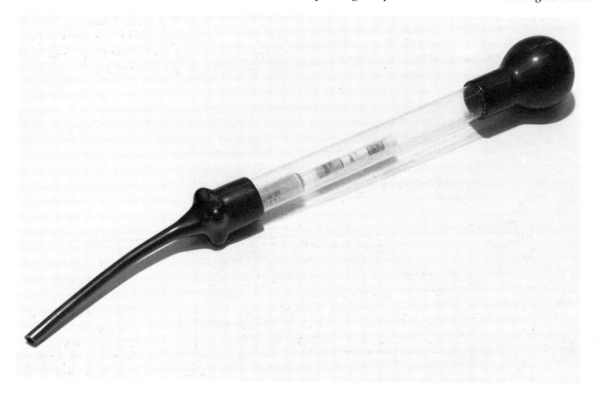

CHAPTER 2
The magneto

The magneto has the advantage of being a completely self-contained device that can easily be driven by the engine to produce the ignition spark.

By the start of the 1920s, nearly all four-stroke engines were ignited by magneto, this practice continuing well into the 1950s. A few die-hard sports models, such as the Gold Star and Velocette singles, stayed on even later with the magneto, although the latter were forced to a coil in the end.

Two-stroke engines also had magnetos at one time, but by the 1930s most (one exception being the Scott twin) had changed to the flywheel magneto or coil ignition. This was to reduce cost but was inevitable anyway as engine speeds rose.

Magneto types

Most of these are Lucas, with some engines fitting BTH, while both Bosch and Scintilla may be found on European engines. Lucas magnetos predominate on British models but come in many shapes and sizes.

Magnetos had a set of standards from their early days when they were always mounted on a platform. This set the spindle height at 35 mm (code letter M) or 45 mm (code letter K) above the platform, along with the other outline dimensions. Over the years, magneto performance went up and their size went down, but the spindle heights stayed the same. Later came the flange-mounted type and after that the rotating-magnet versions.

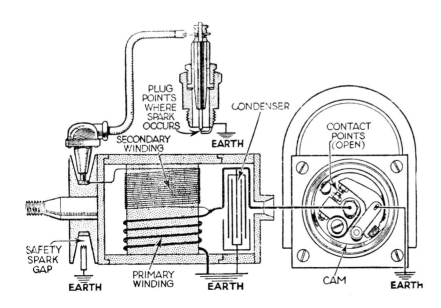

Basic circuit diagram for the rotating-armature magneto with the windings and condenser within

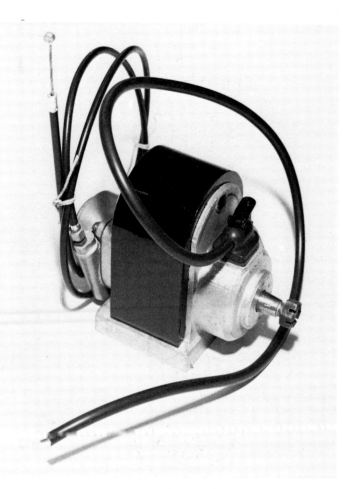

Variations to be found involve the following: the direction of rotation as seen from the driven end; the cam type; whether fixed or manual advance; the fixings in base; competition or racing forms; whether part of a Magdyno; the number of cylinders which, if two, could be parallel, flat or V-twin.

Due to this, any second-hand magneto should be distrusted and checked over accordingly. It is likely to be in need of an overhaul and could well be built up from a selection of parts from a variety of types.

The type of trouble this can bring may be as simple as the internal magneto timing being out. This can be caused by the fitment of the wrong cam, either face or ring, or by the use of points meant for a magneto rotating the other way. Always remember that the points have to open when the flux in the armature is near a maximum and that this is related very exactly to its rotational position. Fit the wrong cam and the points will open when the flux is

LEFT **Earlier type of single-cylinder magneto with external magnet and manual advance**

BELOW **A batch of Lucas magnetos with flange or base mounting, with a rotating-magnet type at top left**

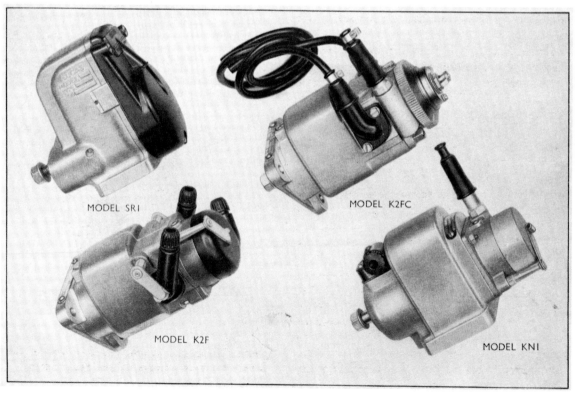

MODEL SR1

MODEL K2FC

MODEL K2F

MODEL KN1

ABOVE Contact-breaker end of early magneto with spring clip to retain the points cover

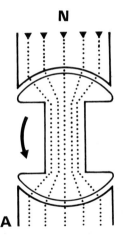

A

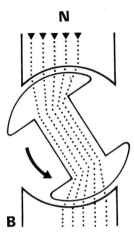

B

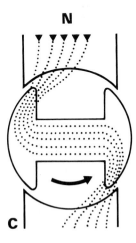

C

ABOVE The manner in which the flux distorts and then collapses to produce the pulse to generate the spark

low and the spark will not be the same even if you get one.

Some further explanation may be useful at this point. The magnetic field created by the permanent magnet (all magnetos have a permanent magnet of one form or another) passes from one magnet pole through the armature to the other pole. Magnetism prefers to travel through iron or steel rather than air or other non-magnetic materials, such as brass, aluminium and some grades of stainless steel, and is measured in lines per square inch—this is the flux. The voltage generated in the coil is not so much proportional to the field strength as to the rate of change of field strength (i.e. the speed at which the field is building or collapsing, or the speed at which the coil is moving through the field). The flux effect (see diagram right) is at a minimum when the armature is central under the poles (A) and increases as the armature rotates. The flux density increases at the tips of the poles—remember that magnetism prefers to travel through iron and therefore squeezes up to one end (B), but as the tip of

the armature pole moves out from under the magnet pole, the flux through the armature ceases and the field collapses, giving maximum rate of change (C). It is at this point that the contact-breaker opens to give a maximum spark. It should be at full-advance here, and when retarded a lesser spark is achieved.

The mounting of the magneto must not be forgotten and neither should its drive system. Flange-mounted units may spigot into a case if gear driven, as this would maintain the drive centres, but where chain is used some adjust-

ment is usually provided. This may be with a slipper tensioner or by moving the unit on reduced-diameter fixing studs.

Platform-mounted units with chain drive normally have slots in the platform so the tension can be adjusted. When gear driven, they are more often located by two or four dowel pins to the platform and the gear centres set with shims under the magneto. Where this is the case, the shims must be retained or the gears will whine in use. On any unknown unit, the gear mesh must be checked and shims added

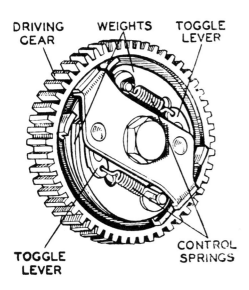

DRIVING GEAR   WEIGHTS   TOGGLE LEVER

TOGGLE LEVER   CONTROL SPRINGS

ABOVE Magneto drive gear with automatic advance mechanism built in

LEFT Douglas flat-twin magneto with its drive from the camshaft and plug lead from each side

BELOW BTH magneto laid out to show construction and ring cam for the points

as required to set it correctly. Beware of damaged locations in the platform, caused by the engine running with the magneto clamp slack—this is a common problem on BSA pre-unit singles.

Magneto service

This routinely amounts to cleaning, checking brushes and setting the points gap. External dirt needs to be removed as it could allow the high-tension voltage to track to earth, causing the engine to misfire.

The brushes need not be checked as often as the points, simply needing cleaning and checking for length and freedom of movement. The points need more regular attention at every 3000 miles and may require cleaning up with a Carborundum stone or silicon-carbide paper. Check for pitting and piling which must be removed, this being caused by the transfer of small amounts of contact material from one point to the other.

The points gap of Lucas rotating-armature

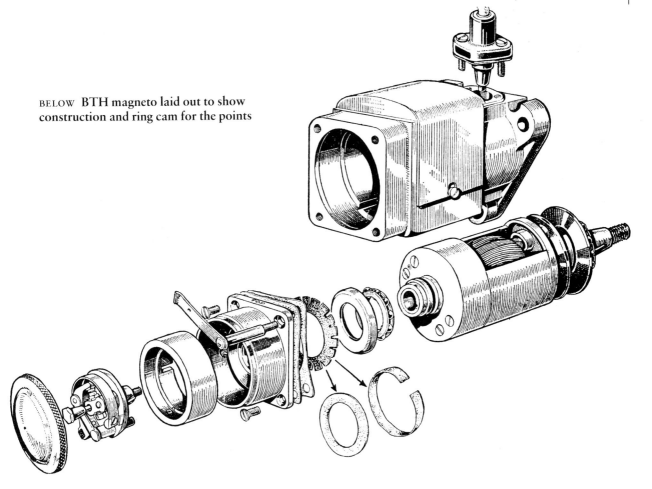

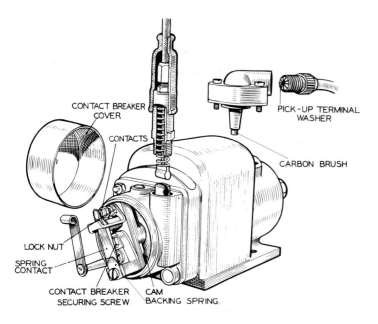

CONTACT BREAKER COVER

CONTACTS

PICK-UP TERMINAL WASHER

CARBON BRUSH

LOCK NUT

SPRING CONTACT

CONTACT BREAKER SECURING SCREW

CAM BACKING SPRING.

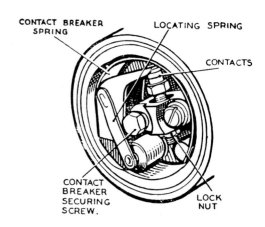

CONTACT BREAKER SPRING

LOCATING SPRING

CONTACTS

CONTACT BREAKER SECURING SCREW.

LOCK NUT

ABOVE **Lucas ring cam with the points plate held by insulated centre bolt**

LEFT **The single-cylinder magneto with manual advance and face-cam points**

magnetos is 0.012–0.015 in. and for rotating-magnet types is 0.010–0.012 in. If nothing is specified for your magneto, 0.012 in. will always be a good figure to use. The gap may be adjusted by means of a screw, with one contact welded to it, and lock nut, or by moving a contact plate which is then clamped in place.

The points-gap dimension given is the maximum separation between contacts and is set at the point of greatest cam lift following the points opening. Don't go further round the cam in case the lift falls away gradually, and check that the gap does not vary due to play or free movement in any of the parts.

Brushes should be examined every 6000 miles, and there are several in even a single-cylinder magneto. First is the high-tension pick-up which bears on the slip ring. This and the flanges on either side of it need to be cleaned using a solvent to prevent tracking.

Check the condition of the pick-up housings, their seals and their fixing, which may be a spring blade or two screws. Examine the high-tension lead and its attachment to the housing. The cable end should pass through a small copper washer, be splayed out and soldered in place—trim off any strand ends.

There will also be an earth brush—this may be hidden under a name or serial plate which must be removed first. If it carries an arrow indicating the direction of rotation, make sure you don't reverse the plate or you could confuse yourself and everyone else. The contact-breaker may have a brush set in its rear face,

while the cover that conceals it may be fitted with an earthing brush.

Points changing

This is normally simple enough to do, but there are several factors to remember. A ring-cam contact assembly has a number of insulating washers, and it is only too easy to leave one out or put it the wrong side of a metallic part to earth the magneto. Always check this point carefully as it is a common reason why some rebuilds don't work.

The BTH magneto has a similar design of ring cam and the same care is needed with it and all its parts. Note that the long spring attached to the moving contact arm should have a small reinforcing spring under each end, held by the small screws.

The Lucas face-cam type has one point on the adjuster screw and the other on the main contact spring. This has a backing spring on top, or outboard, of it and the tag of this must bend away from the main spring. Make sure the insulation pieces are in good order and that the tappet can move freely in its housing. It transmits the rise and fall of the face cam to the contact spring and must be free to return.

Both Lucas types have lubrication wicks which require a few drops of thin machine oil to replenish them. Contact pivots also benefit from a touch of grease, but all lubricants must be kept to a minimum and well clear of the contact points.

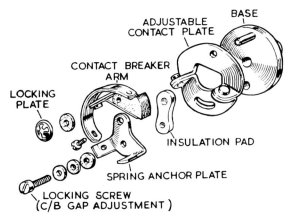

ABOVE **One type of ring-cam points plate exploded to show the detail parts**

BELOW **Twin-cylinder Lucas magneto with flange mounting, ring cam, manual advance and centre button cut-out**

Rotating-armature magneto

Further work on the rotating-armature magneto is rather limited unless you have the right tools and the feel to work with them. Working conditions must be clean and free from grease or oil.

Before you do anything else, locate and remove the safety-gap screw, or screws, as unless this is done you can easily break the slip-ring flange. Be sure to mark parts and make notes so that you know where everything goes, and remember that the contact-breaker housing is often held by four dissimilar fixings. These consist of a hexagon stud carrying a hinged spring arm to hold the cover in place, a hexagon with a wire terminal screw, a countersunk screw, and another designed only to be done up. This last may be sunk in a recess

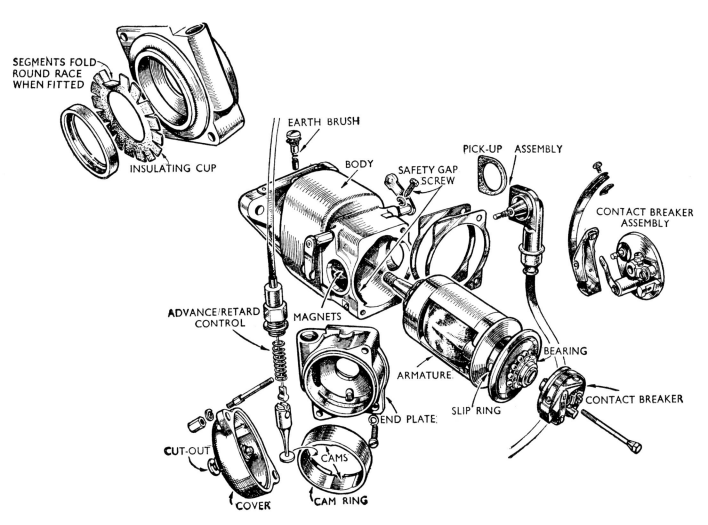

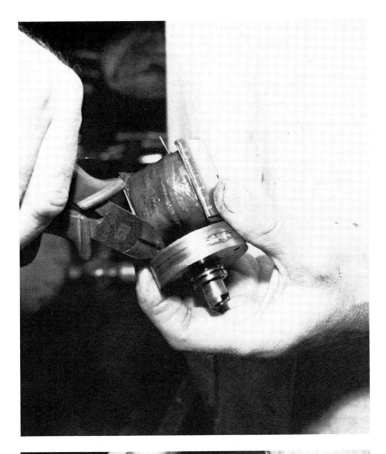

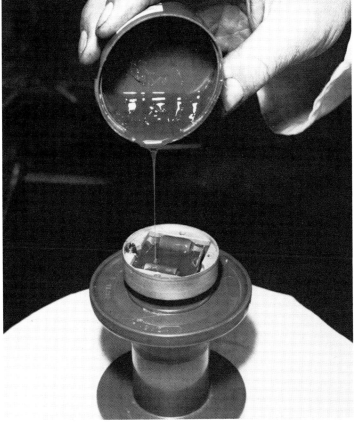

Stages in the replacement of a magneto condenser with the top line showing (from the left) easing off the pick-up ring, undoing the main armature screws, and cutting the condenser lead. The bottom line shows the component parts, the armature end with the new condenser fitted into place, and epoxy resin being poured over the components to seal them into place

and can call for a small pin punch to loosen it.

Before removing these fixings, take off the contact-breaker plate, which is held by a centre bolt, and remove the cam ring or plate. The latter are held by a circlip and marked L or R to suit the magneto rotation. Remove all brushes to leave the bare assembly.

Take out the four fixings to release the end cover which may have shims between it and the body. The armature can now be removed, but the outer races of its bearing will be left in the housings.

The armature

Much of the work that an armature may require is tricky to do, but the most usual task is also the easiest. This is to repair the end thread to which the driving gear or sprocket nut fits. Most will have been maltreated but should clean up with a die—the standard thread was $\frac{5}{16}$ in. or $\frac{3}{8}$ in. Whitworth. Check this as some firms went over to a BSF thread in one of these diameters.

The next stage is to check the windings. Two tests can be employed for this. The first is to wire a 6-volt battery across the armature shaft and its centre at the points end, with an ammeter in the circuit. Refit the breaker centre bolt for this and look for about 4 amps of current flow. Anything else suggests a fault.

For the second test, leave the battery connected and wind a piece of high-tension lead round the slip ring so that it makes contact, holding the other end close to the armature body. Flick the battery connection to complete its circuit at some point, and you can expect a fat spark from the high-tension wire if all is in order.

If you are in trouble it is likely to be the secondary winding, in which case you will need a specialist. The job of winding the thousands of turns of very fine wire, with its interleaving of insulation, requires special skills indeed.

An alternative problem is a failed condenser which causes the points to blacken and burn. As this part is set in the armature, replacement is tricky. You have to remove the slip ring to expose the heads of the two screws holding it all together, remove them and thus the armature end. The condenser is inside this, and only one of the correct value will do, which is 0.2 microfarad and 400-volts dc. It must also be suitable for the duty, fitting the space avail-able, and be adapted to carry a threaded boss into which the breaker plate screw fits. This is an electrical connection as well as a mechanical one, thus adding up to trouble for the restorer.

Other armature problems are repairs to the slip-ring flanges, which can be done with a lathe, good-quality insulating board, epoxy-resin glue and more lathe work. Watch out for wear on the slip ring of a twin which leaves the brass segments proud—it can be built up with epoxy resin and fine machined.

Old magnetos can suffer a deterioration of the shellac coating of their wire, which eventually runs and locks the armature to the body. It may be possible to re-cure the shellac, but renewal with a more modern material is really a better bet. In order to re-cure the shellac, the part needs several weeks of gentle heat—leaving it next to a central-heating boiler has been found to be just about right. Post-war and late pre-war armatures do not have this problem.

Magneto bearings

As these are a variation of the angular-contact type, they work one way only. The outer race comes away from the rest of the bearing and the ball cage normally pops off the inner race. Sizes are in millimetres and range from 5 mm to 20 mm bore, in steps of 1 mm. Widths and outside diameters are not progressive in all cases as the 13 mm bearing has a smaller housing diameter than a 12 mm one, and is also narrower than a 10 mm one.

The bearings often have shims behind the inner race which, together with the body-to-end-plate shims, set the armature free play. Changing the bearings can be awkward as neither inner nor outer will want to come off and both are hard to grip without special tools. The outers also have paper shims round them to insulate the bearings and stop current passing through them, as this would damage the balls and tracks.

End play must be close to nil or the armature may run off-centre and touch the pole pieces—the shims will have to be added or removed to

Running up a magneto on a professional test-rig with variable-speed motor and multiple spark-test gaps

achieve this. A little grease will be needed on final assembly.

Assembly and test

Once the tricky jobs with the armature and shims have been done, assembly is easy enough, being simply a reversal of dismantling to fit the armature, its end cover, the cam, points and brushes. Don't forget the safety screws. Fit the high-tension lead.

Test with the magneto clamped in the vice and the lead coupled to a plug or held firmly about $\frac{1}{8}$ in. from the body. Attach the drive sprocket and advance and retard, and expect the latter to give a poorer spark. Check that the earthing connection, if there is one, does its job. Remembering that magnetos may be asked to run up to 4000 rpm (or 8000 rpm on a two-stroke), this static sparking test is not necessarily conclusive. Misfires, and suchlike, at speed could be mistaken for carburettor problems, and a professional bench test on a rig is advisable.

One check that may have to wait until the magneto is back on its engine relates to twin-cylinder engines and their timing. If the cam ring is worn, it may not open the points at exactly the same point in the cycle for each cylinder—it might also open them by different amounts so that the gap is not the same.

Both these aspects need checking as the engine will perform better and run more nicely if all cylinders have the same ignition setting. Be especially careful when checking a V-twin as the vee angle of the cam ring must match both the magneto and the engine. Vee angles of 42, 47.5, 50, 55, 60 and 90 degrees all exist, with splendid possibilities for error.

It is possible to stone a worn ring to achieve what you want, but this takes a careful hand. It is all too easy to ruin the part.

Should the magneto fail to spark after being renovated, this may be due to poor magnetism. When you turn the armature round, you should feel the pull of the flux as it builds up, especially if the points are removed. If this is poor or non-existent the magneto needs re-magnetizing, which will have to be done by a specialist who has the right equipment for this. It is not good practice to leave the armature out of an old magneto unless a keeper is placed across the magnets.

An unusual trouble, which only seems to occur on BTH twin-cylinder magnetos, is for the magneto to continue to fire the plugs even when the centre screw is earthed. This may occur whether the normal cut-out button is used or a direct contact made and it does not stop the engine running, while the magneto performs perfectly at all times. It would seem to be an obscure winding fault due to old age, as rewinding provides a cure even though no one can deduce why. It can also be caused by a faulty earthing brush.

Magnetos do not like heat very much and this can lead to problems, especially on older units where the magnetism is poor. With these the engine will start and run happily, but then misfire or cut out completely as the heat soaks into the magneto. This is worst when it lives hard up behind a hot cylinder with little cooling air to reach it.

Rotating-magnet magneto

This type of magneto is very much easier to deal with as the windings are fixed, so there are no brushes or slip rings. Check that the wiring is in good order and that the magnets are not loose in the armature, which is very rare.

The main items to check are the points and contacts. Make sure all the small insulating washers go back in the right place when changing the points. Parts are easier and similar to coil or car items, while the condenser could be externally mounted if this proved necessary. The bearings are still of the magneto type, so there are shims under the end plate and the same requirements and problems apply. An exception to this is that the outers do not have insulating cups round them, thus being a little easier to remove and replace.

There are two important don'ts with these magnetos. Don't remove the cam or you may lose the internal magneto timing unless you mark parts very carefully indeed. Don't obey the 'Remove to oil' instruction found on the distributor rotor of some twin-cylinder types. The part came from a car distributor and the note does not apply in the motorcycle application.

Details of the Lucas SRR1 rotating-magnet magneto with fixed components. The lower drawing shows a twin-cylinder model

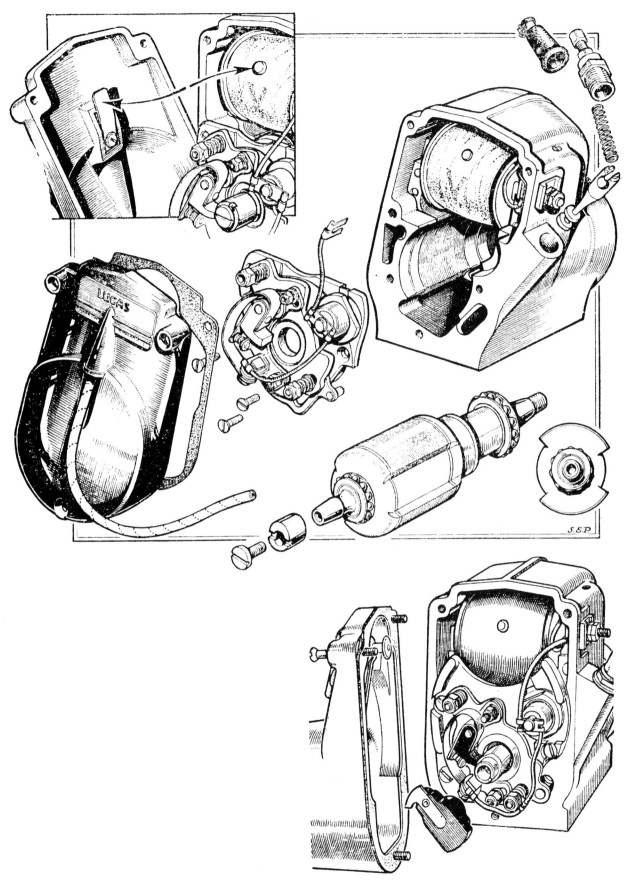

Maglita

This was an ingenious attempt to combine the magneto with a generator, first produced by the ML company and then taken over by Lucas. It featured on some Rudge and BSA models right up to 1938, but nearly all who have had experience of it have disliked it.

The revolving part formed the dynamo armature and included a centrifugal cut-out to connect the current once the device reached speed. Two brushes and a simple commutator gave a direct output. The magneto winding, magnets, points and condenser were stationary and drew their power from the same armature winding.

The device functions by splitting its output

A Maglita combined magneto and dynamo which was a nice idea but did not quite come up to expectations

between the two halves; but to do this it has to be run at engine speed with a reduced advance and retard. The magnets need a keeper if the armature is removed and it is likely that many troubles arose from poor magnetism. Both the spark and the lighting were poorer than normal, so don't expect too much from this system if you have one. It also produced a spark at every revolution, and a blow-back through the carburettor, causing a fire, was not unknown. Owners should therefore fit a gauze flame-trap to the carburettor intake.

CHAPTER 3
Coil ignition

The battery-powered coil-ignition system has been in use for many years and is simple and easy to deal with. Basically, the battery has to connect to the correct end of the coil, with the other coil terminal connected to the points and condenser. The only moving part is the points cam and its advance mechanism.

The points gap of most systems is 0.015 in., and the system can sometimes be used to check out a machine by providing a simple basic ignition. This may be used with a battery without any other electrics and can help in determining whether the trouble is ignition or carburation. A small motorcycle battery will provide enough energy to power such a system for 200 miles or so, which is quite sufficient for testing.

Points service

Where the points are mounted on a fixed plate, they only need inspection, cleaning or replacement and re-gapping. The clamp screw must be in good order and the most common trouble is to muddle the insulating washers under the spring end, thus shorting the circuit to earth.

Make quite sure the wire from the coil and that from the condenser connect correctly. If the condenser has to be changed to one that will not fit the space available, it can be moved elsewhere, perhaps next to the coil. Electrically it makes no difference.

The points plate can usually be rotated a small amount to set the timing and must also be flat and fit into its recess nicely. Twin-cylinder machines may have one or two sets of points and, if the latter, one or both may be movable on the backplate to set the timing. If only one moves, then the fixed one is timed first to allow the other to be adjusted to match.

Behind the points will be the advance mechanism on most makes, although Bosch has this outside the points plate. In either case, the effect is the same with the cam, on its bearings, being able to move round the drive spindle which is driven by the engine, usually from a camshaft. The two are connected by weights and springs which have to be correct for the engine type.

The bearings can cause problems as wear will allow the cam to move about, varying both the points gap and the timing. If this is bad, replacement will be the only answer. The small pins and links in the centrifugal mechanism can also wear and upset the advance curve. The same problem arises if the springs are tired. It is common for two different springs to be fitted as this gives an initial rapid advance, so check before changing what looks to be incorrect.

Distributor or contact housing

Strictly speaking, only assemblies with a rotor arm and distributor cap carrying high-tension leads are distributors. However, the term is commonly used to cover contact housings, as used by the BSA C15 and others, where the assembly only includes the points, whether for one or more cylinders. What distinguishes the type is the incorporation of a centrifugal advance mechanism in the body.

In either case, there will be a top cap to clean and, where it is a distributor, to check for

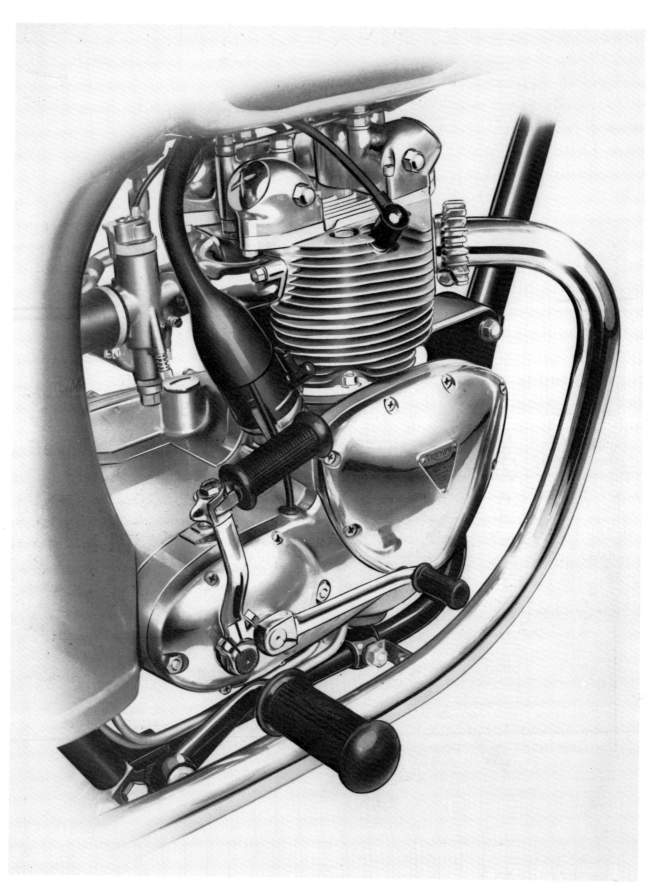

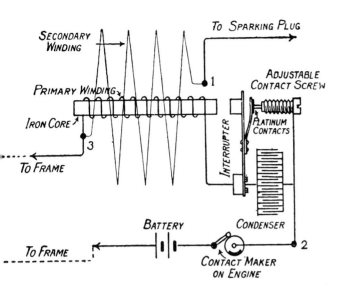

ABOVE Circuit for trembler-coil ignition, as used on some of the earliest machines

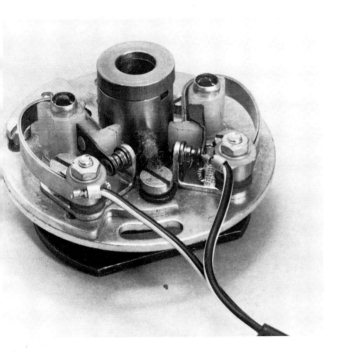

ABOVE Points plate for twin-cylinder machine with only one set able to move relative to the backplate

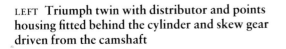

LEFT Triumph twin with distributor and points housing fitted behind the cylinder and skew gear driven from the camshaft

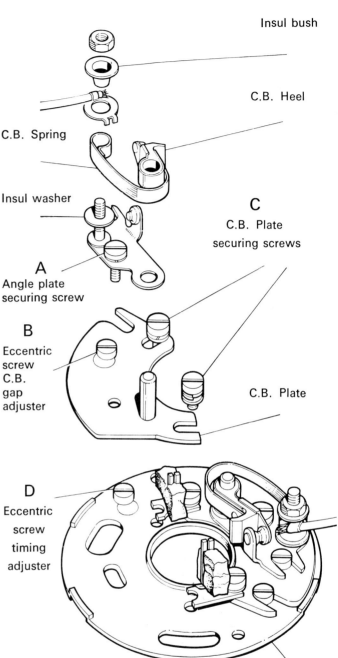

ABOVE Component parts of twin-cylinder points plate where both sets can be moved for timing

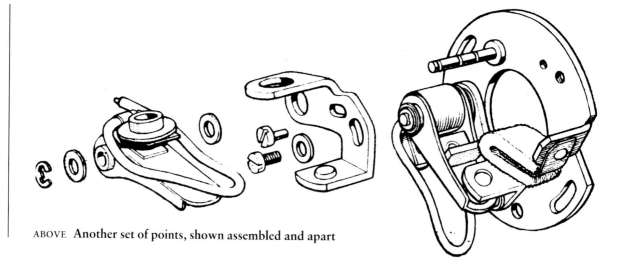

ABOVE **Another set of points, shown assembled and apart**

MODEL DKX1A

MODEL D1A2

MODEL 15D1

MODEL CA1A

MODEL 2CA

MODEL 18D2

MODEL DKX2A

MODEL DKX4A

cracks and wear on the centre brush. Under it will be a points plate which needs to be flat, has to fit, and have good threads for the points themselves. The plate is usually fixed in one place as the complete housing may be turned to set the ignition.

The advance mechanism will be under the points plate, or above it for Bosch equipment, and is more prone to the effects of wear as the drive spindle has its own bearings in the housing. These can allow the cam to wander quite easily, due to the height of the cam above the bearings. Otherwise, the renovation, advance springs and small pins are as for the more directly driven type.

All parts need to be clean, and the spindles need a drop or two of oil. Again, the condenser can be mounted elsewhere if this solves a problem. Make sure the low-tension lead makes a good connection and that all the insulating washers are present and correctly placed. Check that the rotor arm is in good condition, ensuring that it is not cracked and is a tight fit on its driving spindle.

Alternative methods of driving the distributor were used on Ariel Square Fours and Royal Enfield twins. These had the assembly located at the driven end of the dynamo, with gearing to turn the cam spindle. This fitted in neatly to provide the coil-ignition facility in a compact and inexpensive form. It followed earlier arrangements for singles, where the points were mounted on the end of a dynamo driven at engine speed. In this application the extra, unused spark did not seem to be a problem.

The coil

This must be of the correct voltage for the system, with due allowance for any special circuit features. It must be clean, correctly

ABOVE **Lucas distributor and points housing with automatic advance mechanism**

LEFT **A variety of points housings, distributors and points plates, as used for coil ignition**

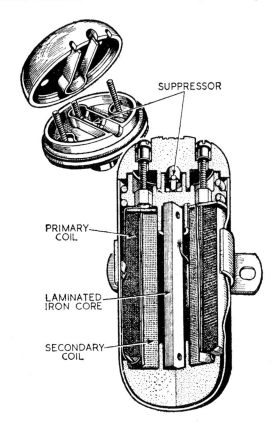

ABOVE **A Wipac ignition coil showing typical construction of the in-line form**

Later Wipac coil with terminal nuts and high-tension lead socket

mounted and with its wires securely connected to the correct terminals. It will work if these are the wrong way round, but not so well.

The majority of coils used will be 6- or 12-volt, but on occasion may be two 6-volt coils in series, as on some Norton twins. Both 3- and 9-volt coils exist, so treat anything unknown with suspicion.

Some engines were supplied with rather inadequate coils; if you suspect this, or that your coil is not up to par, it may be worth changing it for a more modern one or a car type. Modern coils use a full iron loop rather than a bar and are far more efficient. Coils can also suffer from heat.

In all cases, make sure the high-tension lead is securely held to the coil and is reasonably waterproof. The need for this depends very much on the installation and varies from one machine to another. Thus, one with the coil hung out in the rain with water dripping on to it from the tank will run without a falter, whereas another, seemingly well protected, will misfire in the damp.

The lead may be held by a screw with a spiked end or other means. Often it is simply pushed into the end of the coil, but this design can be developed as in the Bosch type. Popular with road racers at one time, this had a collet form of clamp to secure the lead and seal it, plus an outer back-up rubber cover. It worked very well.

A combined assembly

The LE Velocette in its early years fitted a BTH generator on the front of the engine that combined dynamo, regulator, ignition coil, points, and distributor into one unit. An advance was built into the points-cam drive, and the distributor was driven by a gear pair within the assembly.

As with any other generator, it needs to be kept clean, the screws tight and the leads in good order. The points gap is 0.012 in. and this was thought important enough for Velocette to include a gauge for setting it. This was sprung into a recess within the generator body rather than supplied in the tool kit. The gear pair must be correctly meshed or there will be problems, and a special tool is listed to remove the advance unit if this has to come off.

This generator type was superseded late in 1953, but was listed for another year or two.

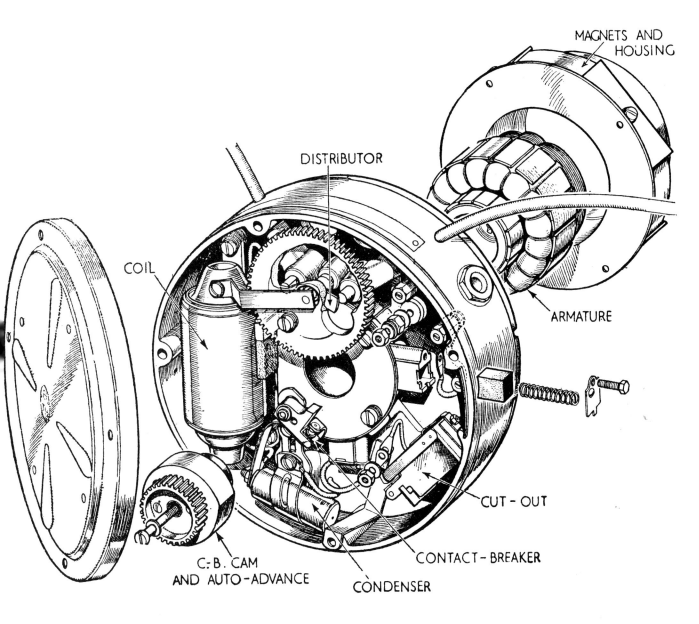

MAGNETS AND HOUSING

DISTRIBUTOR

COIL

ARMATURE

CUT - OUT

C.B. CAM AND AUTO-ADVANCE

CONTACT - BREAKER

CONDENSER

Condenser

If this is beginning to fail, there is likely to be a misfire at high speed. As it worsens, though, the problem occurs at a lower engine speed. In the end the engine will start and rev up in neutral, but misfire badly as soon as any load is placed on it. At the same time there will be severe sparking at the points, which will suffer.

Test by substitution as the electrical test equipment needed to check the item is rather complex. Beware that your replacement is not faulty by further changing it to work on an engine known to be running as it should.

Make sure that all connections are sound and that there is an earth path back to the battery as well as to the supply.

Generator as fitted to the early LE Velocette, with all the functions combined into one compact unit mounted on the front end of the crankshaft

CHAPTER 4
Flywheel magneto and ET

These are both a form of rotating-magnet magneto, with the first common on two-stroke engines and the second used for competition four-strokes. Both tend to be particular about their internal magnetic timing and have their own sets of problems.

Using a special holding tool while undoing the centre nut of an ignition rotor

Servicing flywheel magnetos

There is not a great deal to do other than checking for damage, making sure the connections are secure and setting the points gap. In most cases the parts are keyed in place, so there can be little or no variation in timing, whether internal or ignition.

Older types may be best served with a keeper

plate if the rotor is removed, but this is not necessary on modern units. Rotor removal may require a special puller which should be used to avoid damaging the parts. The rotor nut is designed, in some cases, to pull the part from its taper, and so it will undo a turn or two and then go tight again. Further work with the spanner will break the taper joint.

Of course, there are always the ones which do not have a thread for a puller and whose nut puller design is not up to the job. If this is the case, you will have to resort to some form of 'controlled violence' with drift and hammer. This can be worked by winding the nut out to load the pulling device as much as it will take without breaking, and then using a drift on the centre of the shaft. One really good thump, nice and straight into the shaft, should move the rotor, but tapping it will not be good enough. Expect it to let go with a real bang!

The fit of the rotor to the shaft should be checked and improved by lapping if necessary. The rotor must run true as it is a fair size and when run at engine speed will cause serious vibration if it is not right. Do not lap too much or the rotor will move in on its shaft and may then touch the stator.

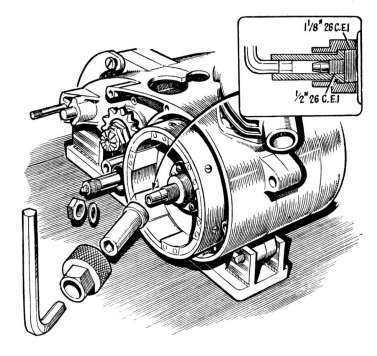

ABOVE **Special puller used to remove the rotor from the crankshaft of a small Royal Enfield**

BELOW **Villiers points adjustment and cover as on the older style of engine**

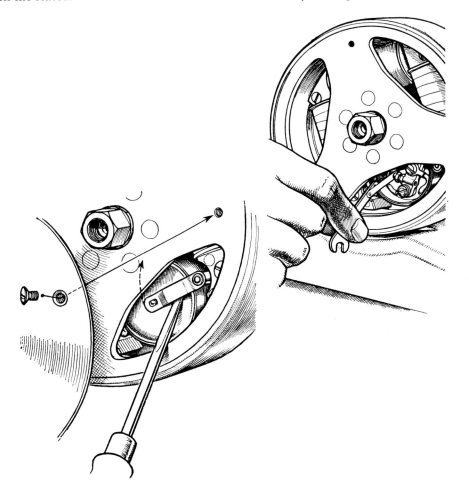

Both the ignition and the generated current for the lights and battery will be affected by the air gap between the rotor and the poles of the stator. This has to be a minimum for the best output but must be enough to cater for manufacturing tolerances on the parts and any flex in the driving shaft when the engine is running. If the stator assembly is a poor fit to the engine crankcase, generator output can be varied by moving it about. This is not good practice, though, and well-fitting parts are always to be preferred.

Flywheel-magneto problems

Magnetism, heat, coil size and condenser sum up the reasons why so many two-stroke owners have had troubles with magnetos and starting.

These are the areas to move on to once you are sure the points have the correct gap and the connections are as they should be.

The magnets can lose their magnetism. Rectifying this is a specialist job due to the equipment needed, but the process can make all the difference, turning a unit that will only fire on the finest of days into one that goes in just about any conditions.

Heat can be an enemy and builds up as the engine warms up. Thus, as with the magneto, the machine will start and run for a while before fading to a standstill. It will then refuse to start until it has cooled down, by which time the plug will be oily. Once this had been cleaned, though, it fires up and repeats the whole cycle.

One of the great attractions of the flywheel

magneto was that it was self-contained. It could be bolted to a two-stroke, or four-stroke, with ease, its high-tension lead running straight to the sparking plug. Thanks to its symmetrical pole-and-magnet layout it could easily be adapted to a twin, and it was also no problem to add further generating coils to supply the needs of the battery or the lights. This made it especially useful to firms that supplied engines to others since it kept the whole assembly as a nice neat package without odd extras.

Unfortunately, it also meant that the ignition windings had to fit within the rotor, hence the whole coil became restricted in size. This was especially so for the compact assemblies needed for clip-on engines and mopeds, although their lighting needs were somewhat less, which helped.

The answer was to move the ignition coil outside the flywheel magneto, powering it from a low-tension coil similar to the generating ones. This allowed the use of a much larger ignition coil, and a good number of engines built over a period of years made this change.

Condenser problems and effects are much as for magneto or coil ignition, and replacement is the usual answer. As with the coil, it is easy enough to fit an alternative part elsewhere and connect it to the circuit with a lead.

Energy-transfer ignition

A flywheel magneto with external coil is a form of energy-transfer (ET) ignition, but to many owners the term applies to a troublesome design used on competition or off-road singles. In it, a special alternator provides the power and is linked to a special ignition coil.

The system operates with the alternator coils connected to the points and the ignition coil, which are in parallel and not in series as is more usual. While the points are closed, the generated current passes through them as this is its easiest path. When they open, it is forced to change direction to the coil in a pulse; this induces the high tension in the secondary winding connected to the plug.

The problem is that the magnetic timing has to be just right or the pulse will not be at its peak when the points open. An error either way

Alternator, points plate and ignition coil for the unloved Lucas energy-transfer ignition system

will result in a weaker spark, this problem being aggravated by the need for ignition advance on a four-stroke.

Early versions of this system were used by Triumph and BSA, who soon found that what was fine on an experimental machine was just too fussy for the private owner. Few understood why or how the system worked anyway, and all the designs had the points in a contact housing rather remote from the crankshaft.

The build-up of tolerances made a mockery of precision, and the skew gears in the drive added their own backlash in the train. The result was either an engine that would start but not rev, or one that would rev but not start—or not without a push. Works riders in trials events soon became tired of this—they kept going by restricting the advance angle and being very careful with the points gap and the alternator-to-points timing.

Road models followed suit, but the system was fraught with this trouble and in time was replaced by others. It can be made to work with careful attention to the above details but may wander away from the optimum in use. The alternator stator used in this system may have anything from two to six coils: two are for the ignition and the others are for lighting. Where just two are fitted, they will provide direct lighting without a battery in the manner of a flywheel magneto. With three coils, the extra one is used solely to supply a stop lamp, while four coils are fitted if a battery is used on the machine and has to be charged.

Some of the rotors used with this system have more than one keyway or dowel hole in them. They must be fitted correctly or the engine will either run badly or not run at all.

Lucas

This firm concentrated on its traditional range of magnetos and dynamos with the addition of the alternator in the 1950s. It was not until well into this period that they produced a flywheel magneto, which was in an energy-transfer form with external coil.

The coil was in fact mounted on the rear of the stator on the 6F1 unit which was made for mopeds. The operation was as for the normal energy-transfer system, but with the direct mounting of the parts there was not the problem of keeping every section in time.

This unit later became the 7F1, which was

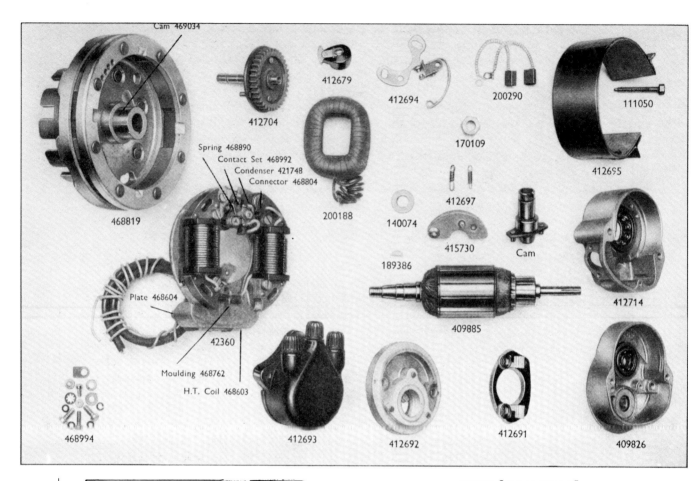

Cam 469034
412679
412694
200290
111050
412704
170109
468819
412695
Spring 468890
Contact Set 468992
Condenser 421748
Connector 468804
200188
412697
140074
415730
Cam
189386
412714
Plate 468604
42360
409885
Moulding 468762
H.T. Coil 468603
468994
412693
412692
412691
409826

ABOVE Less common Lucas flywheel magneto and dynamo with distributor, as in their parts list

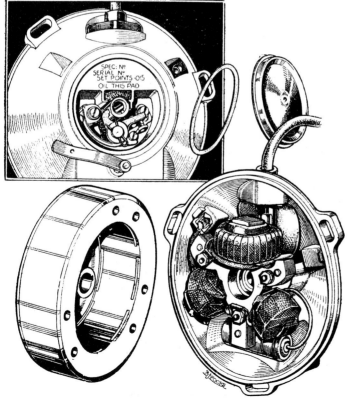

LEFT The Wipac Geni-Mag, as used by the first BSA Bantams, with small access cover

RIGHT The later Wipac magneto for the Bantam, as used for many years for direct- or battery-lighting models fitted to some Raleigh mopeds and had a 0.015 in. points gap. In this form the coil had moved back into the assembly in the usual manner, but the unit did not remain in the range for much longer.

Wipac

Most owners know this make through owning a BSA Bantam at one time. It differed from other flywheel magnetos in having the stator outboard of the rotor but operated in exactly the same way as any other. Its contact points were, however, far more accessible, as it was not necessary to work through cut-outs in the rotor to reach them.

The first type was called the Geni-Mag and was available in 6- and 12-volt forms with an early user, in 1947, being Motosacoche. A year later it appeared on its first Bantam and featured on this model up to 1966.

The original Geni-Mag had a small points cover set in the centre of the stator and a high-tension insulator in its top. A spring clip held the cover in place while the whole stator could be moved through seven degrees for timing adjustment. The ignition cam was keyed to the end of the crankshaft which was supported by a porous bronze bush set in the stator. If this is worn, it needs to be replaced.

The Geni-Mag was soon replaced by the Series 55 Mk8 which had a much larger points cover and a rubber-sleeve wire outlet set further round its edge. This is the type that most Bantam owners are familiar with and it is easier to service than the original.

Both have problem areas, but once these have been dealt with the unit is a reliable one. If neglected, however, it will play up. The points gap is 0.015 in., but if it will not run at this, needing something smaller, there are two possible reasons. One is that the rotor magnetism is down and the part needs re-magnetizing. The other is that the cam has been changed.

At one time, a 'retarded' cam was available that allowed the timing to be nearer top dead centre without losing spark efficiency. Prior to this, it was necessary to cut the mounting slots away and clamp the stator in place if a high-compression cylinder head was fitted, calling for the timing to be retarded. The special cam gave the same result while keeping a good spark.

A common fault is for the pin on which the contact arm pivots to work loose in the casting. If this happens, the gap will vary wildly and

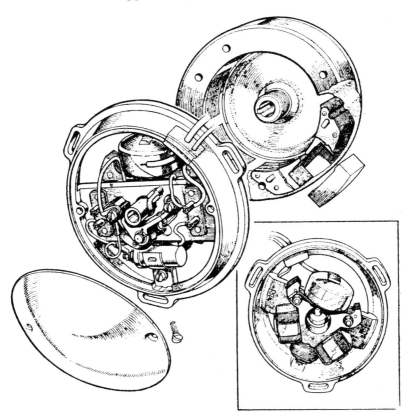

the engine will either not start or not run. The remedy is to make a new pin which screws into the housing, fitting this with Loctite. By removing the stator armature which carries the coils, and cutting some of the casting away, it becomes possible to add a lock nut to the new pin to make sure. This alteration became standard practice on racing Bantams.

The connections need to be clean and in good order, while it pays to make sure that the contact rocker arm does not come too close to a clamp screw, thus shorting out. The same applies to the circlip which holds the arm in place and the easy answer is just to leave the clip off. The main spring will hold the arm in place.

To remove the rotor you must use the correct puller. This screws on to the thread formed on the rotor boss and pushes against the shaft end. It must fit round this, so don't use the original tool which had a pointed draw bolt, as this will ruin the crankshaft end. To overcome this problem, the centre screw was counter-bored to fit round the shaft end. For this to work you either have to remove the cam key or must let it sink into its keyway. This inevitably runs into the centre tapped hole—the key is always damaged by the screw and so in many cases needs to be replaced along with the screw.

The final point to check is the fit of the stator in its mounting and the air gap between it and the rotor. The fit is often poor and thus the centre bush becomes the location—this is fine as long as the crankshaft is in line. The output from the generating coils can be altered by moving the stator about, and some dealers would do this until the output at the engine speed equivalent to 30 mph in top balanced the full light load.

Around 1951 a racing version of the magneto was produced for the Bantam. This only had one magnet, plus a counter-weight, in place of the usual three, plus a more robust centre. There were no lighting coils and the cam was special, with a shorter opening period, but otherwise the construction was as for the standard unit.

The original design was developed into the IG Series 73 for the Excelsior Talisman twin, and in this form was enlarged a little to accommodate a distributor disc and board under the cover plate. The cam became a double one, so the single coil and contact points remained along with lighting coils.

Wico-Pacy also built a smaller Migemag, later the Bantamag, for clip-ons and mopeds. This differed in having the stator inboard of the rotor, with an outer cover held in place by a wire clip. It was of simple construction and is easy to renovate, unless it is low in magnetism.

This was replaced by the Series 90 Bantamag

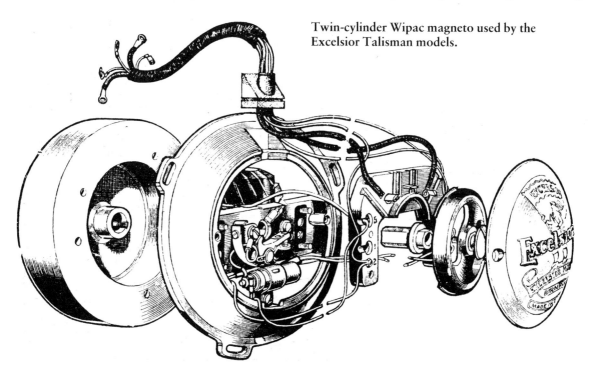

Twin-cylinder Wipac magneto used by the Excelsior Talisman models.

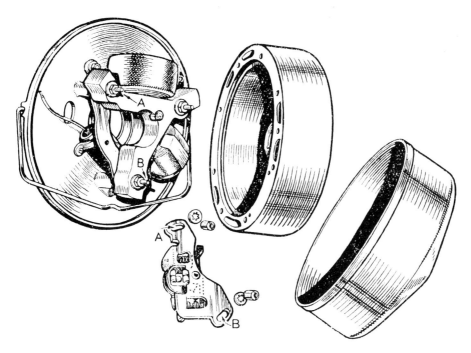

ABOVE Wipac Migemag for cyclemotors with ignition and lighting coils

BELOW The Wipac Bantamag which replaced the Migemag and was also used for clip-ons and mopeds

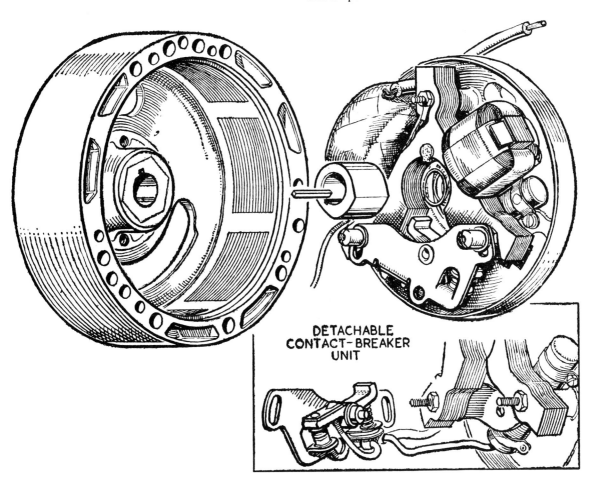

DETACHABLE
CONTACT-BREAKER
UNIT

which was similar in form. The Series 90 had its cam separate from the rotor in order that the latter could be removed while setting the points, unlike most of this type.

In time, the IG and Series 90 went from the Wipac range, but the BSA Bantam continued with its flywheel magneto for many years with the internal coils wired to suit either direct or battery lighting.

Miller

The FL18 Miller flywheel magneto was fitted to the Royal Enfield wartime Flying Flea and the post-war 125 cc model derived from it. The construction was similar to that of the Wipac Geni-Mag, with the stator outboard of the rotor and a small cover over the points and condenser.

There were two lighting coils and one ignition coil, but the supporting bearing for the crankshaft was a 10 mm bore ball race. The cam was a taper fit on the shaft without a key and had an internal $\frac{5}{16}$ in. BSF thread to assist its removal. A special tool was needed to pull the rotor off.

The points gap was 0.010 in. to 0.015 in. and the usual rules on wiring and connections apply. The ignition timing was $\frac{5}{32}$ in. to $\frac{3}{16}$ in. before tdc, and of equal importance was the

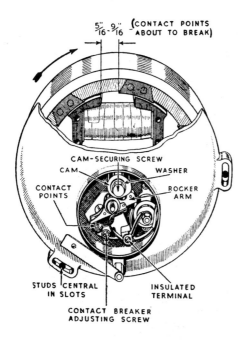

Miller magneto as fitted to the 125 cc Royal Enfield in its early form

relationship between the rotor and the ignition coil. It was required that the trailing edge of the moving pole piece had passed the tip of the left side of the core lamination by a given amount. This was given as $\frac{5}{16}$ in. to $\frac{9}{16}$ in. for the wartime model and $\frac{1}{8}$ in. for the post-war model built up to 1950. The stator fixings were slotted to allow this.

In addition to the FL18, the firm also produced the FWX for autocycles which had the rotor outboard of the stator. The cam was formed as part of the rotor, which meant that the points had to be set working through the windows in it. This can be tricky as the magneto may try to pull at your feeler gauges and screwdrivers. The latter may become magnetized in the process, which can be useful or not.

The firm also offered the FL27, which was similar to the FL18, and went on to add the W7, without lighting coils, and the W8, with lighting coils, both much as the FWX. The FL18 type was joined by the ER1 with greater generator output, plus another version for a twin.

For 1951 the firm had two new units for specific models, while the W7 and W8 continued and the FWX became the FMC. Of the two new units, one was the RE2 which went on the 125 cc Royal Enfield which had received a face-lift. In its new form it was more enclosed than before, but, more importantly, it had an external ignition coil mounted on the frame. The cam remained on its taper on the crankshaft with the same internal thread for its extraction.

The rotor boss had a $1\frac{1}{8}$ in. × 26 tpi Cycle thread, which the extractor needed to remove it, and the correct tool uses the $\frac{1}{2}$ in. × 26 tpi Cycle thread on the crankshaft for the rotor nut. One half of the tool screws on to each thread and then the inner is undone to pull the rotor off.

The second new unit in 1951 was for the LE Velocette flat twin and listed as the AC3. It was a little unusual in that the stator had coils on both sides with three generating ones at the rear and two ignition plus points and condenser on the front. The rotor went behind the stator and the cam, and its advance mechanism was attached to the crankshaft nose.

The ignition system was in fact coil with both plugs fired together to give an idle spark. The battery powering the system was backed

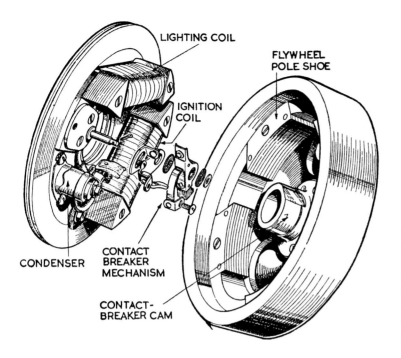

LIGHTING COIL

FLYWHEEL
POLE SHOE

IGNITION
COIL

CONDENSER

CONTACT
BREAKER
MECHANISM

CONTACT-
BREAKER CAM

LEFT Miller FWX flywheel magneto for autocycles

BELOW The Miller RE2 design, fitted to the later Royal Enfields, which had an external coil that improved its performance

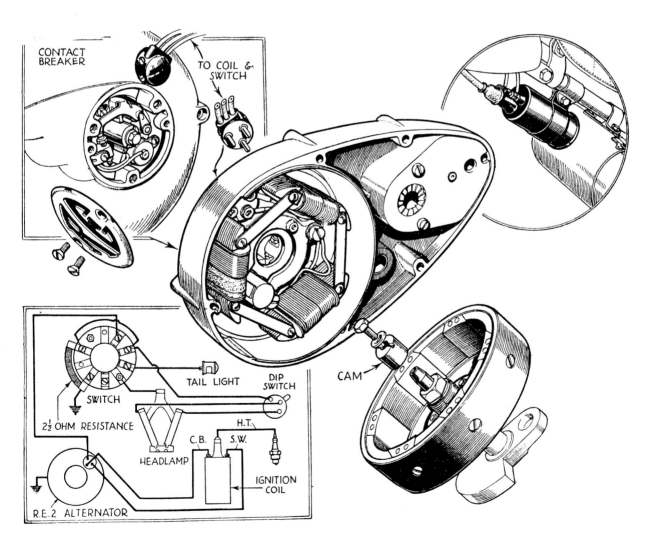

CONTACT BREAKER

TO COIL & SWITCH

CAM

SWITCH

2½ OHM RESISTANCE

TAIL LIGHT

DIP SWITCH

HEADLAMP

C.B.

S.W.

H.T.

IGNITION COIL

R.E.2 ALTERNATOR

47

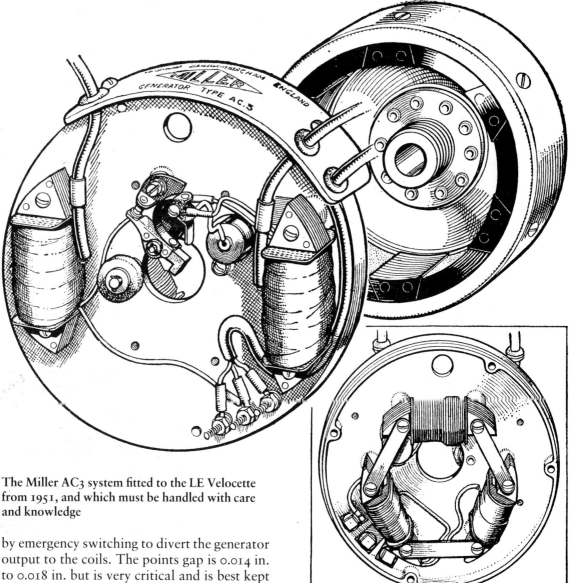

The Miller AC3 system fitted to the LE Velocette from 1951, and which must be handled with care and knowledge

by emergency switching to divert the generator output to the coils. The points gap is 0.014 in. to 0.018 in. but is very critical and is best kept as close to the larger figure as possible. The rotor needs an extractor to remove it and must be timed to the crankshaft. A dowel hole indicates this, when the pistons need to be at tdc.

If the battery connections of the AC3 system are reversed, the rotor magnets lose their magnetism. Due to this, the design was modified on the AC3P which had a circuit-breaker built in to prevent this happening. The engine will run in this form if the incorrectly-connected battery has enough current to supply it, but the generator will not charge.

Within two years, the Velocette was fitted with the AC4 which included a ballast resistor in the supply line to the coils. The range of flywheel magnetos continued and was augmented with others, some being adaptations, to

increase the range. All were similar in design and will respond to cleaning, inspection and renovation.

Late in the 1950s, the moped unit was revised so that the rotor was smaller, and both the ignition and lighting coils were positioned outside it in the manner of their alternator. Their housing was spigoted to the crankcase and carried a plate outboard of the rotor for the points and condenser.

The use of Miller flywheel magnetos tailed off in the 1960s when the 125 cc Enfield disappeared from production in 1962 and the LE changed to Lucas equipment in 1964.

BTH

In addition to the unit built for the early LE, this firm made a flywheel magneto for the Douglas Vespa scooter built in the UK. This was of conventional form with outboard rotor incorporating the cam. The points gap was 0.012 in. and the backplate carried two lighting coils as well as the ignition components.

The unit was fitted to the early 125 cc models known as the Rod type for 1951–53 and the G for 1953–54. It was also an alternative for the GL2 of 1954–55, but a Piaggio unit was fitted from then onwards.

Villiers

This company built engines for many uses and would therefore design them so that parts could be easily changed round to alter the specification. From 1922 they used their own flywheel magneto and adopted a similar policy for this item. Thus the rotor may have two, four or six poles and the stator can carry anything from one to seven coils.

All have the rotor outboard of the stator, a few have a remotely-mounted contact-breaker, some have an external ignition coil, and they come in various sizes. A cooling-fan ring was fitted to the rotor for scooter or small-car use and both single- and twin-cylinder versions were built.

Problems are mainly concerned with connections and settings, but the unit is prone to fading when it gets hot, usually due to poor magnetism. The condenser can fail but may be replaced by an externally-mounted part, and the high-tension connection which screws into the rear of the backplate can leak electrically or when it rains.

The basic construction of many Villiers magnetos is much the same with a substantial rotor held in place by an extractor nut. When undone, this will turn and then try to release the rotor from the mainshaft. Further rotation will complete this and Villiers recommended using their Hammertight spanner for this job or when fitting the rotor. Rotors were not keyed but were marked on the rim and the backplate. The marks should align at tdc which will give the correct ignition timing.

The number of magneto poles increased to four in 1932 and to six a short while later, but there are several varieties of the latter. This is because some of the magnets may be dummies, only fitted to balance the assembly, while the pole shoes may also be dummies. The numbers and layout in relation to the ignition cam peak are important and are dependent on the engine and its use. Note that it is possible to dismantle these rotors, but if the parts are mixed the magneto may well decline to spark any more— this is a point worth checking on an unknown rotor.

On the six-pole magnetos, the air gap should not exceed 0.020 in. or be less than 0.004 in., so the various parts need to run true and be well located. The rotor fits on a 1:10 taper which is ground to suit as there is no keyway. It is secured by a nut with right-hand thread, but two sizes have been used so there are two Hammertight spanners. The points gap is 0.015 in. in just about all cases.

Using the Villiers Hammertight spanner to release the centre nut, which was often self-extracting

Villiers magneto types

The earliest flywheel magnetos went on the MkIV engine and had two poles to provide ignition only. The unit was referred to as the 'large' type as the rotor was $8\frac{1}{4}$ in. in diameter. Later versions had coils for direct lighting. For the MkVI-C 147 cc engine, a smaller 7 in. version was used, with or without lighting coils.

During the 1930s, first the four-pole and then the six-pole magnetos were introduced, the latter becoming the standard design. In it the number of magnets was varied, as was the number of coils, with separate ones for the head and tail lamps to give independent circuits.

This last type was available with 18- or 24-watt headlamp output which was achieved with a change of rotor width. This was $1\frac{1}{8}$ in. or $1\frac{7}{16}$ in. respectively, but the same stator plate was used in both assemblies.

A three-pole magneto providing ignition and direct lighting was introduced for the 98 cc Junior De Luxe engine and can be fitted to the older Junior. This had a two-pole magneto, but if this is changed the light bulbs will need changing as well.

The 98 cc 1F and 2F engines have a common six-pole rotor with four magnets and two dummies. Both ignition and direct-lighting coils are fitted but the 1F has two of the latter and the 2F only one. The second coil allows for the use of rectified lighting, but if it is not used then either coil, by itself, is used for the direct circuit.

With the introduction of the 4F unit in 1953, the contact-breaker was divorced from the magneto and moved to the left end of the crankshaft, along with the condenser. This allowed a reduction in the diameter of the rotor, but the stator continued to carry one ignition and two lighting coils as on the 1F type. Both direct- and rectified-lighting versions were made, this practice continuing for the 6F type brought in for 1956.

In later years, the 98 cc engine was joined by the 50 cc 3K unit which had its flywheel magneto on the left end of the crankshaft. It had an outboard rotor while the stator assembly included the points and condenser with the ignition coil and single lighting coil.

The 122 cc D-class engine began as the MkVIII-D in the 1930s and became the 9D just before the war. A six-pole magneto of 18 or 24 watts was fitted depending on the user's specification. For 1949 it was replaced by the 10D which fitted a similar magneto with six magnets and five iron and one dummy pole shoes. The dummy has to be fitted to be just ahead of the ignition cam peak, which is to the left of the centre line of the cam when viewed from inside. Two lighting coils were fitted and the same assembly served both direct and rectified types, although the connections from the magneto differed.

The 12D, which replaced the 10D for 1954, had the same magneto with detail improvements. It was joined by the 11D which was a competition version, thus having a special ignition coil in the magneto. The cam also differed

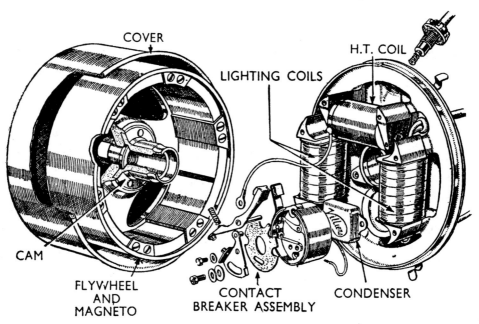

COVER

LIGHTING COILS

H.T. COIL

CAM

FLYWHEEL AND MAGNETO

CONTACT BREAKER ASSEMBLY

CONDENSER

and had a reduced points open period, while the assembly had a sealing ring at the rim of the cover.

The 147 cc 29C and 30C engines used the same magnetos and cams as the 11D and 12D units, but the 148 cc 31C introduced in 1956 differed. It followed the lines of later engines with the magneto fully enclosed and the points separated from it. A six-pole rotor was retained and still went on the right of the crankshaft, but there were three lighting coils plus the ignition one on the stator. Direct or rectified lighting could be obtained from the same assembly.

The ignition cam was keyed to the right-hand end of the crankshaft, outboard of the rotor. It was retained by a circlip and should be a light push-fit on the shaft. The points and condenser were mounted on the right outer cover that enclosed the magneto, with a small plate giving access to them.

The 173 cc 2L engine used the same arrangement as the 31C, as did the fan-cooled 3L used by some scooters.

The early 197 cc 3E and 5E engines used the same magneto as the MkVIII-D and 9D, while the 6E of 1949 adopted that of the 10D but with a wider and heavier rotor. The 7E and 8E copied the 11D and 12D in both magneto and cams, while a high-output version was available for the 8E.

A new 197 cc unit, the 9E, was introduced in 1955, which was soon joined by the 10E with vertical cylinder and 11E for use in scooters. All used the same arrangement as the 31C with the cam keyed to the end of the crankshaft.

A little earlier, for 1954, the older style of engine was joined by the 224 cc 1H, which was much as the 9E but had an externally-mounted ignition coil. The stator plate carried four coils, two for ignition and two for the lights and battery charging. The ignition cam remained on the end of the crankshaft and a cut-out switch with key was mounted in the right cover. This functioned by connecting the points to earth to cut the ignition.

In 1957 the 1H was replaced by the 246 cc 2H which was much as the twin-cylinder models, while retaining the ignition key in its right side cover. This had a larger recess for a circular points plate and room for two condensers, although only one was fitted. The stator had three coils, equally spaced, with one for the ignition and the others for the lights. The external ignition coil was the same type as those used on the twins, but although it looked the same, it did not interchange with that fitted to the 1H.

It was soon superseded by the 246 cc A series which appeared in 1958 and was very similar in design to the 9E. It thus repeated the magneto type used on the 31C and 2L and continued in use until the late 1960s.

For 1963, the A series was joined by the 247 cc Starmaker unit which was built for road or competition use. The ignition arrangements were external coil with points carried on the right engine cover in most cases. For road racing, a special self-contained points assembly was offered which bolted in place of the normal contact plate. A separate shaft with its own

LEFT **Earlier form of the Villiers flywheel magneto, which came in many models with working or dummy magnets**

BELOW **Special self-contained points unit fitted to the racing Villiers Starmaker engines**

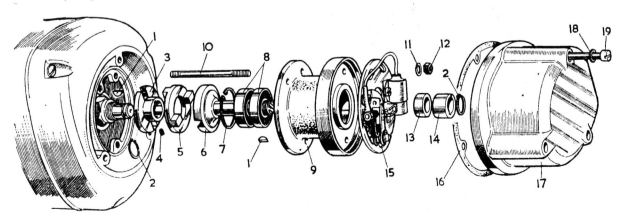

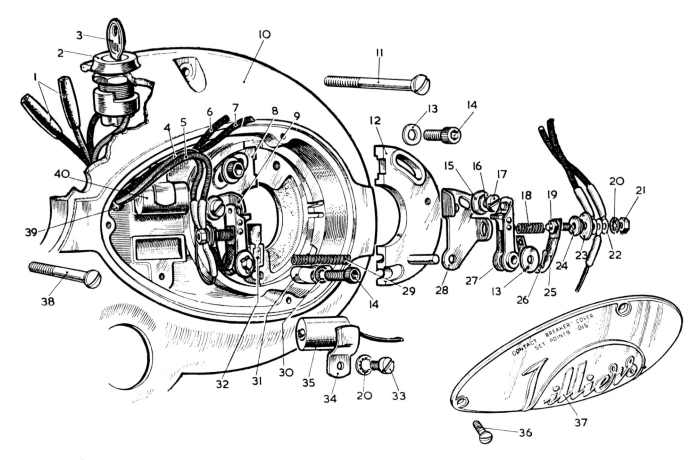

bearings carried the ignition cam and was driven by a coupling whose inner section keyed to the end of the crankshaft. This arrangement removed some of the sources of points bounce from the ignition system.

A six-arm stator was fitted but the number of coils depended on the specification. All had the ignition pair but either 6-volt direct lighting or 12-volt rectified lighting could be added. The first has three lighting coils, with one for the stop light and two for the main lights and the horn; the other has four lighting coils.

Finally, the 249 cc twin-cylinder engines listed as the 2T and 4T, plus the 324 cc 3T— with regard to ignition, all are much as the 2H except that four coils are fitted, as on the 1H.

Engine points arrangements of Villiers twin with split mounting plates for ease of timing adjustment

The ignition coils are externally mounted and the ignition cam keyed to the right end of the crankshaft. Each set of points is mounted on a separate plate, enabling both gap and timing to be individually set.

In addition to at least two versions of the standard circuit, the 4T could also be had with a high-output generator. With this the ignition coils were powered by the battery, so all four stator coils could be used for charging, using twin rectifiers and a charge control switch.

CHAPTER 5
Electronic conversions

Electronic ignition came into use on the racing scene in the 1960s to cope with the needs of high-speed two-strokes and was later fitted to many vehicles in order that they could comply with the emission controls in the USA. This was not so much for the better combustion achieved but more to cope with the need to run for lengthy periods without adjustment.

Since then, the basic idea has been refined and developed to a high state of sophistication and control, thanks to the advances in electronics, micro-processors and mini-computers. Along with breakerless systems, there were also those that retained the contact points but restricted the current through them so their life was greatly extended, and others that used the alternator to power the system and thus dispense with the need for a battery.

All types were offered in kit form for most popular machines and can often be found in the course of a restoration. In addition, some restorers like to change to a more modern ignition system to improve its efficiency and may also seek to do this without detracting from the machine's external appearance. This is easier with some systems than others, but electronic ignition is generally more compact now than it was in earlier days.

Assisted points

This system has the great advantage in that if it fails you can return to conventional coil ignition to get you home. You will need the normal condenser to wire across the points, but it is not difficult to arrange a change-over switch to alter the connections at will.

The ignition will continue to suffer from the variations of any cam-and-points system but will not burn its points. The electronic box can usually be tucked away out of sight and should be kept out of the rain anyway.

As always, good connections are vital.

Alternator-powered system

This Lucas type retains the points, which have to work as hard as usual, and adds a capacitor and zener diode. It enables the engine to run with or without a battery and with or without lights.

The system is based on 12 volts and takes the output from all three pairs of alternator coils, joined in parallel, to the rectifier. The positive output from this is earthed and the negative becomes the feed to the battery, lights, capacitor and ignition coil. The zener diode connects from the same line to earth to control the system.

In operation, the alternator charges the capacitor to store the energy for the ignition coils, and the change when the points open induces the high-tension spark. The capacitor has to be mounted with its connections pointing down and must be connected the correct way or it can easily be rendered useless.

This system is easy to adopt and works well with most six-pole alternators, except those designed for energy transfer. The system means that the rest of the electrics have to be changed to 12 volts but this is a good move on most machines, while the whole idea is a great help

LEFT Triumph twin, fitted with the coils for a Boyer ignition system, awaiting the top plate with the magnets

RIGHT Lucas Rita electronic system with box, trigger housing and other parts

BELOW RIGHT Boyer electronic system fitted to a Norton twin's timing cover, with the trigger plate to one side

BELOW Capacitor mounting for points-controlled system, using the alternator to provide the power

to the owner of an off-road model—it was for them that the system was conceived but it has also proved useful to others.

Systems without points

These are the type used by many modern engines and are usually triggered by a magnetic pulse or a light-emitting diode. Both the devices fulfil the purpose of contact points and cause the electronics to spring into action.

The power for the system may come from a battery or alternator and generally all work in a similar manner. The power source charges up a capacitor which is then switched by a thyristor, also known as an SCR. This is a special form of diode which acts like a switch and turns on when it receives a short electrical pulse from the trigger. The capacitor then discharges into the coil primary which induces the desired secondary spark.

These systems may have fixed or variable timing, with the advance achieved electronically. With the latter, any mechanical advance in the drive must be removed or locked up so that it does not interfere with the electrical changes. The timing itself can only be roughly set mechanically, after which it must be set

MOTORCYCLE FRAME

using a strobe at the correct speed which can be up to 5000 rpm. The strobe may show a little more advance above this speed and also some at tickover. The latter occurs because the electronic advance commences from zero rpm, thus having moved up a little at idle.

These system kits come with very full instructions which must be fully and carefully followed. Most problems occur because this

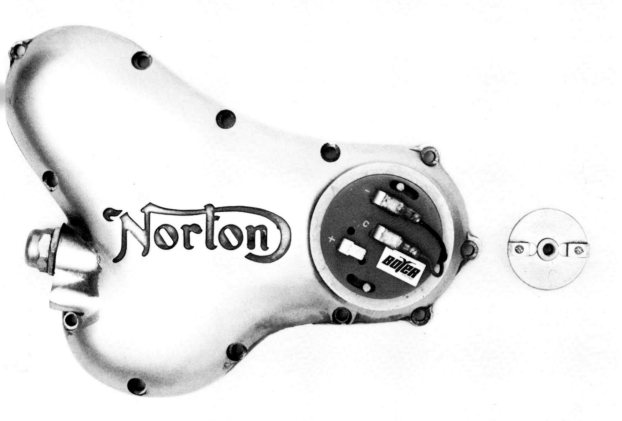

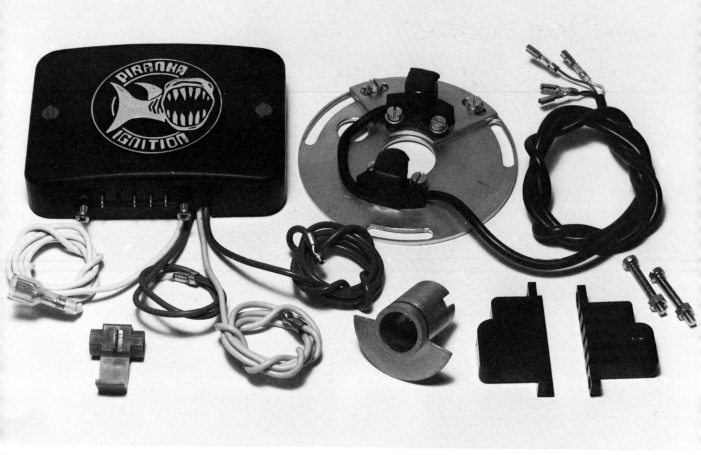

ABOVE **The Piranha electronic system with ignition trigger based on light-emitting diodes**

LEFT **Krober system uses fixed magnets and rotating arm to trigger the spark**

has not been done and a stage in the work has been skipped.

If you have machining facilities, it is possible to adapt a kit to fit on to a rotating-armature magneto, but some care will be needed to set everything up correctly. The most important point with a twin is that the triggers must be at 180 degrees or the timing will be out and impossible to correct.

The position is easier with the rotating-magnet, SR-type Lucas magneto as this can be modified to take a Boyer Bransden unit within. The external appearance remains unchanged and the system is for 12 volts only. As with all such systems, it has to have the timing set by a strobe with the engine running.

CHAPTER 6
Ignition timing and sparking plugs

These two subjects go together and are often of some concern to restorers. The first is usually the subject of much careful research and debate, while the second brings with it problems of translating the data of the past into today's range of plugs.

Ignition timing

In a sense this is very important, but the original figure for your engine may be less so. This is because the engine is now middle-aged, worn in various ways, may have an alternative piston fitted, could have sunken valve seats, and is running on modern fuel rather than that available to it when new.

All this makes the original figure a good starting point but little more. From it you may have to make adjustments to obtain good running without pinking or lack of power. An old-fashioned technique that can still work well is to run the machine on full throttle on a rising road, while advancing the ignition until the engine pinks. You then back it off a little to prevent this, but remember that the fuel used and general engine condition must allow pinking to occur. If the motor is soft and you run it on high-octane fuel, it may refuse to respond to this form of test. The method is easier to use on some engines than others, depending on the ignition drive and whether you have manual control of the timing or not.

Setting and checking the timing

To set or check the timing you must first find the engine top dead centre, whether you take your measurements with a degree disc or in terms of piston movement with a dial gauge. The latter is the normal way for the ignition timing of a two-stroke, but on four-strokes either method is common. The disc should be fitted to the drive side of the crankshaft and a rigid pointer set to read from it. Note that the disc needs to be large enough and the pointer thin enough to allow an accuracy of one degree or less to be obtained.

Lock the disc in something close to the correct position and then check how far out you are. This can be done by introducing a stop down the plug hole, but is better done with the head off and the stop across the top of the barrel. Turn the engine slowly until the piston gently reaches the stop and then note the disc reading. Reverse the action until the piston again comes up to the stop and take the second reading.

The measurements should be in degrees from a zero, at tdc, and are added together and the result divided by two. The answer is the position the disc must be moved to while the crankshaft stays where it is. Then recheck it to make sure it is correct.

The same result can also be achieved with a dial gauge set in line with the cylinder and acting on a fairly flat area of the piston top. In this case, zero the gauge at maximum piston height and check the disc reading about 25 degrees either side of tdc. When it is the same, the pointer is correctly set.

The points gap must be set correctly before the timing is attended to, and due note must

57

ABOVE Using a timing disc and feelers at the points to check the exact moment they will open and the plug will spark

BELOW The alternative to the disc and feelers is the dial gauge working on the piston crown and a bulb wired across the points

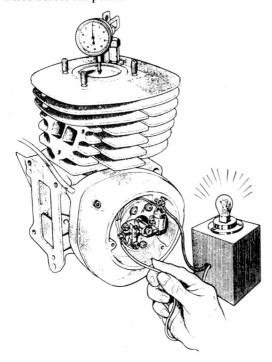

also be taken of the special problems of a twin or where the points gap is varied to adjust the timing. The way the timing is set varies from engine to engine, but the common aim is that the points start to open when the piston is at some distance before top dead centre.

On a four-stroke or a multi, make sure you work with the right set of points, the correct cylinder and the right engine stroke. Ensure you turn the engine in the normal direction of rotation and beware of backlash in the drive to the points cam.

The moment at which the points start to open can be checked with a small bulb wired across them, a meter, or the traditional fag paper. Use the thinnest of the last and turn the cam until it will just slide out between the points.

On many engines the timing is set by positioning the crankshaft or piston at the desired number of degrees round or inches down and then turning the cam to the point of opening. The drive gear or sprocket is then pushed on to its taper and the nut holding it must be done up. It should then be checked in case it has slipped at all.

Some engines are easier in that the points plate or housing can be moved to adjust the

LEFT **Checking the points gap of one of the three cylinders of a Trident**

BELOW **The contact breaker of a Villiers flywheel magneto and the timing marks on the crankshaft and rotor**

timing. For these the ignition cam can be secured and the engine turned to its firing position. The points plate is then rotated until the light or meter shows that the contacts have separated.

Multi-cylinder engines may have a set of points for each cylinder or a cam, with a lift for each and sometimes a distributor. All should be checked on each cylinder on full advance and retard. Correct timing on full advance is important on all engines, and for multis it should be the same for each cylinder as this will give smoother running.

Where a cam ring or one with lobes is used, it may be necessary to stone this to achieve the identical timing. If there is a set of points for each cylinder, these should each be adjustable. If one is on the main plate and the others on separate plates, adjust the main-plate timing first and then the others. If all can move, the job is easier. Should all the points be fixed to one plate, the timing can sometimes be adjusted by varying the points gap. However, this is limited in its effect as the gap tolerances still apply and the job can be tedious to do. In this case, a modification to separate points plates is well worth making up, and a later assembly can often be adopted, provided the

cam size and lift are similar.

Some engines have timing marks to aid setting and to indicate tdc, but the careful worker will always check that these mean what they say. Others have location pins and slots or

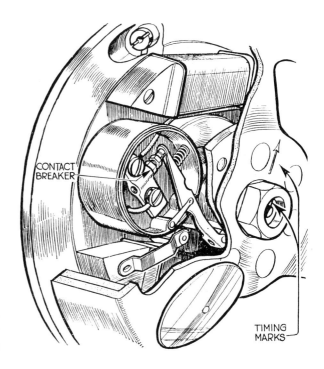

CONTACT BREAKER

TIMING MARKS

holes in the flywheel and the same rule applies in case something has been altered at any time.

Many Villiers engines have a timing line on the rim of their magneto rotor and a fixed line on the crankcase. Such engines have no rotor key but are timed by aligning the marks when the piston is at tdc. This is easy to locate and the marking allows for the required ignition timing ahead of the dead centre. It can then be checked with a rod down the plug hole after the centre nut has been tightened, using the Hammertight spanner favoured by the firm.

Engines built in the late 1960s or later often had timing marks included, usually on the alternator rotor. A marker pin would be included in the rotor cover which allowed the timing to be checked with a strobe. Any engine can have this facility once a marker and scale have been devised to show the position of the crankshaft as it turns. This has to be set up using a degree disc and any timing marks found should be checked in the same way. Checking is easy from then onwards, and the xenon strobe powered by an external battery is the best choice of equipment. It is much brighter and thus easier to use than the neon type which plugs into, and is powered by, the high-tension lead.

This same method is used to set electronic-ignition systems as few have any way in which the point of triggering can easily be detected. They thus have to be set approximately in the correct place so the engine will start and run. The timing can then be adjusted, but the only way it can be checked is with a timing mark and a strobe.

It is just as important that an electronic system be correctly timed on full advance as any other. In either case, timing marks for both advanced and retarded ignition settings are needed, and it is the former that is the important one. Remember that the engine must be run fast enough for the advance mechanism, whether mechanical or electronic, to reach its full throw. Some electronic systems do not do this until 5000 rpm, which always sounds more than you think. If you do not get this right, the engine could have too much advance at high speed—which could lead to burnt pistons and other troubles. As always, don't run the engine for long periods in a closed garage for obvious health reasons!

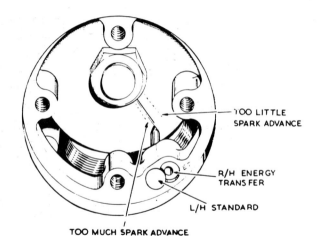

ABOVE Timing pin and rotor mark used with a strobe to check the ignition timing with the engine running

RIGHT Using a strobe light with the timing disc on the camshaft in this case

BELOW Detachable sparking plug which can be dismantled for cleaning

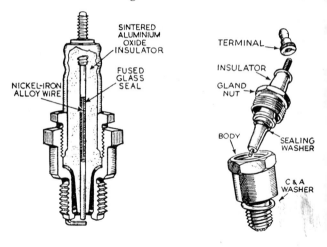

Sparking plugs

These come in a variety of sizes and have been sold under some 2000 brand names over the years, many of which were quite obscure. In post-war years, most motorcycles were recommended to use something from the Champion, KLG or Lodge list in the UK, Bosch in Germany, and Champion again in the USA. There were also many others, such as AC and Wipac, and now the market is dominated by the Japanese NGK and ND firms.

All have their own code systems, which have become quite extensive, to cope with all the many varieties now possible, but in earlier times all that was usually needed was the thread

diameter, the thread length and the heat range.

The thread diameter can be 10 mm, 12 mm, 14 mm or 18 mm which covers most people, but there is also a $\frac{1}{2}$ in. one used for farm and marine equipment and a $\frac{7}{8}$ in. one used in the USA in the past. Most motorcycles that a restorer is involved with will have either 18 mm or, more likely, 14 mm plugs. Odd exceptions do occur, though, such as the LE Velocette which always fitted 10 mm plugs.

The thread length used in motorcycle engines was commonly $\frac{1}{2}$ in. (referred to as 'short reach') or $\frac{3}{4}$ in. (termed 'long reach'). There were others with $\frac{3}{8}$ in. lengths occurring on some 14 mm plugs, plus other odd lengths with some of the less usual thread diameters.

The heat range was something all makes of plug had in common and related to the speed at which the centre electrode and its insulation lost heat. This variation arose due to the need for the plug interior to operate at a temperature that was high enough to burn off any deposits, but not so high as to cause pre-ignition. The actual electrodes also needed to be kept as cool as possible to minimize their erosion and thus extend the life of the plug.

Plugs were thus graded from soft (or hot) to hard (or cold). The first had a long heat path from electrode to plug body, thus retaining its heat to be suitable for soft, low-output engines that tended to be oily and needed the temperature to burn oil deposits away. The hot plug had a short heat path and therefore cooled rapidly—it could thus cope with high-compression ratios, more heat and high combustion-chamber temperatures. It is, however, less able to burn oil deposits away and can more easily oil up. This is less of a problem with electronic ignition as the very high plug voltages that these systems generate can also burn the excess oil away.

The plug you fit must be of the correct length. If it is too long, it will protrude into the combustion chamber and its inner threads will clog with carbon. It will then be impossible to remove without at least taking the head off, and it is also possible for some types to clash with a high-compression piston.

If the plug is too short, the electrodes will be masked, which may affect the performance. In addition, the unused threads of the plug hole will be covered with carbon, so when the correct-length plug is fitted it will jam. The cure is to remove the head and run a tap through the plug hole. At the same time, check that the seating face is clean and square to the thread, otherwise you may have a gas leak.

Old-type plugs could be dismantled for cleaning but this job needs to be tackled with care if you attempt it. Do not try it with the mica insulation of pre-war KLG plugs as this will fall apart, but the lower part will still dismantle. For some plugs, the sealing washer may need annealing if solid, which can be done by heating it to cherry red and dropping it into water.

A machine in frequent use should be fitted with a modern plug, this being renewed in the usual way. An old one may be kept for 'show', but be wary of running the engine on it in case it cracks internally and drops a piece of insulator in your motor.

A minor point is that the current reaching the plug is direct and thus the centre electrode can be positive or negative, depending on the circuit. The first requires a rather higher voltage to make it spark and therefore it will erode at a faster rate. A 360-degree twin with magneto will have one of each, due to the way the windings function, and thoughtful owners swap the plugs over every 2000 miles or so. If left in the same cylinders all the time, they will look very different as they near the end of their useful life.

Plug cap

These come in a variety of shapes and may have a suppressor built into them. Some are waterproof but most simply shroud the top part of the plug insulator. They are best kept away from the magneto ignition, as the increase in the suppressor resistance with age gives the magneto more of a problem in firing the plug. In the end, it may be unable to do this.

Check that they are in good order and a nice tight fit on to the plug. There must be a good mechanical and electrical connection to the high-tension lead, and all dirt or grease should be cleaned away. Inspect for cracks or any other possible paths for the high voltage to leak to earth. If it can, it will always do this in preference to jumping that small gap in the cylinder!

RIGHT **Sparking plug in section to show internal construction**

FAR RIGHT **Plug and cap which may often house a suppressor as well as making the connection**

CHAPTER 7
The dynamo

Dynamos were first offered for motorcycle use back in the Edwardian era, and the Lucas 'Mag-dyno' appeared at the start of the 1920s. Regulation of its output changed from third-brush to compensated voltage control, or cvc, around 1936, and post-war this system ran on into the 1960s.

A dynamo produces direct current and can therefore be directly connected to its control unit and hence the machine battery. It actually generates alternating current, as do all mechanisms that produce electricity from mechanical movement, but this is converted into direct current by the commutator built into the end of the armature.

Dynamo drive

This can be by chain or gear and may include a friction clutch to protect the dynamo from sudden changes in engine speed. This feature is included in the Mag-dyno on the magneto shaft and can be found on any machine with this type of electrics.

The Mag-dyno and its clutch are normally fitted to single-cylinder four-strokes, while parallel twins more usually keep the two instruments separate. Some singles also do this, in which case, on both twins and singles, the drive is more often than not direct and without a clutch. Some degree of shock insulation is provided by the chain or gear train from the engine to the dynamo. One twin that did keep the clutch was the Norton Dominator, which had this built into the drive gear attached to the rear of the camshaft sprocket.

The Lucas Mag-dyno with gear drive between the two parts and to the magneto

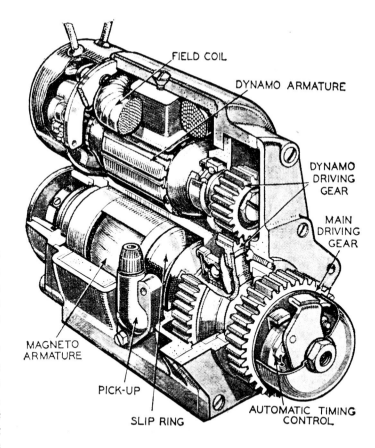

FIELD COIL

DYNAMO ARMATURE

DYNAMO DRIVING GEAR

MAIN DRIVING GEAR

AUTOMATIC TIMING CONTROL

SLIP RING

PICK-UP

MAGNETO ARMATURE

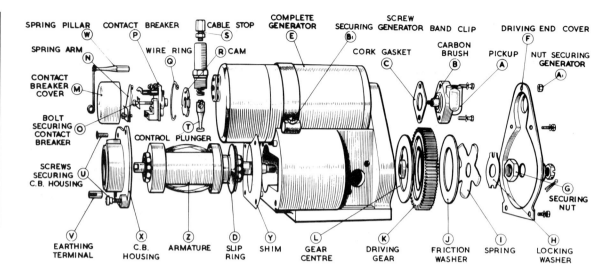

SPRING PILLAR   CONTACT BREAKER   CABLE STOP   COMPLETE GENERATOR   SCREW SECURING GENERATOR   BAND CLIP   DRIVING END COVER

SPRING ARM   WIRE RING   CAM   CARBON BRUSH   PICKUP   NUT SECURING GENERATOR

CONTACT BREAKER COVER   CORK GASKET

BOLT SECURING CONTACT BREAKER   CONTROL PLUNGER

SCREWS SECURING C.B. HOUSING

W   P   S   E   B1   F

N   Q   R   B   A   A1

M   C

O   T

U   G   SECURING NUT

EARTHING TERMINAL   C.B. HOUSING   ARMATURE   SLIP RING   SHIM   GEAR CENTRE   DRIVING GEAR   FRICTION WASHER   SPRING   LOCKING WASHER

V   X   Z   D   Y   L   K   J   I   H

ABOVE Exploded view of Lucas Mag-dyno used by many makes and models over the years

RIGHT The Lucas E3H dynamo, with ball race at one end and bush at the other to support the armature

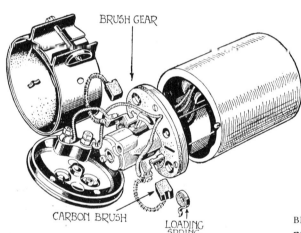

BRUSH GEAR

COMMUTATOR

STEEL PINION

ARMATURE

CARBON BRUSH

LOADING SPRING

Any drive system should be checked over for mechanical damage and repaired or replaced as necessary. Sprockets or gears must fit well on the armature and be keyed in place. Fixing nuts must be in good order, together with any means of locking them.

Lucas drive clutch

This fits on the magneto armature with the rear plate keyed in place. A fibre gear fits against this with the front plate, a simple ring, and the clutch spring. The spring has five fingers and locates round a pin pressed into the rear plate.

A lock washer and nut complete the assem-

BELOW Locking tool needed to enable the clutch nut to be undone on a Lucas Mag-dyno

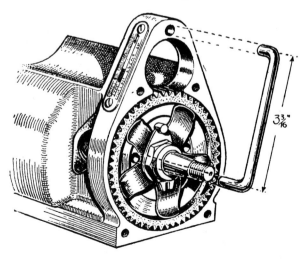

3³⁄₁₆"

bly with the clutch-slipping torque set by tightening the nut. Once adjusted, it is locked by the washer which also locates to the pin.

To turn the nut it is necessary to hold the armature still, and to assist in this the rear plate has extra holes drilled in it. A tool for this can be made from a piece of $\frac{1}{4}$ in. rod bent into a U with 3.2 in. centres. Do not try to lock the fibre gear for this job as, firstly, it may slip, and secondly, you could damage its teeth.

Check the clutch working faces of both the plates and the gear to make sure they are smooth. The torque setting is 4–10 lb ft, but something in the region of 8 lb ft is a good target. In this case it will be necessary to lock the fibre gear, and a small diamond-shaped piece of metal, $\frac{5}{16}$ in. $\times \frac{11}{64}$ in., will do the trick.

The gear pair should be lubricated with a high-melting-point grease. If this is packed around the dynamo gear, it will distribute itself on to the teeth of both gears in the required amount. Avoid over-greasing.

Running tests

There are some checks that can be made while the dynamo is complete and either on the machine or on the workbench. The tests may not give complete answers but can offer quick guidance to a problem area.

The test on the machine is carried out by joining the field (F) and dynamo (D) terminals, and connecting a voltmeter from the join to earth. The engine should be run slowly, as the dynamo output is no longer regulated, and at about 1000 rpm dynamo speed the voltage should have risen smoothly to a reading of 10 volts.

Do not run the engine faster or you could damage the dynamo. If there is no reading at all, the fault is most likely to be with the brushes or connections. Should about 0.5 volts appear, the field coil is suspect—and if 1.5–2 volts appear, it is the armature winding which may be faulty.

With the dynamo off the machine, the same test can be carried out in reverse. Again the D and F terminals are connected and the join taken to the battery supply terminal. If the dynamo body is joined to the battery earth, the armature should motor round in the normal dynamo direction.

These tests can be carried out as described where the cut-out is a separate unit, but if it

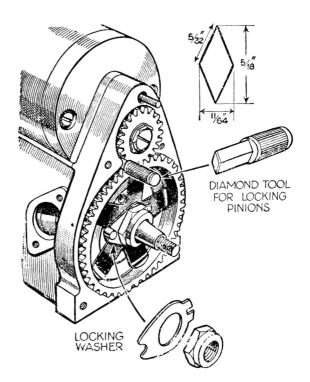

DIAMOND TOOL FOR LOCKING PINIONS

LOCKING WASHER

Tool used to lock the Lucas drive gear to set the clutch torque

is built into the end of the dynamo it will have to be held closed or bypassed.

Servicing

This concerns brushes, bearings, commutator, and the general condition of the parts and electrical connections and wiring. Access to them is straightforward in most cases, but remember that some items may be brittle and easily cracked.

The dynamo is usually held together by two long screws, with the ends and centre dowelled or keyed for location. The fit of the ends into the body is important because it controls the concentricity of the parts and any slack will affect the air gap. This exists to avoid damage to parts but must not be excessive.

The brushes are held in contact with the commutator by springs and it is these which need to be lifted up to release each brush in turn. Do not pull the brush lead as it may come adrift. Each brush needs to be inspected for cracks and for a nice glaze on its working end. Make sure it can move easily in its housing and is not worn too much. In an extreme case, the

ABOVE Running a Lucas dynamo on a professional test-rig to check its performance

BELOW The end plate of the Lucas third-brush dynamo used by many makes during the 1930s

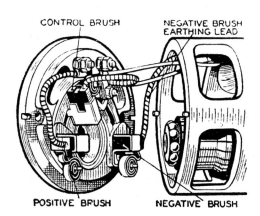

CONTROL BRUSH   NEGATIVE BRUSH EARTHING LEAD

POSITIVE BRUSH   NEGATIVE BRUSH

spring would then press on the housing rather than the brush.

A new brush should be checked for its fit in its housing once this is clean. Any grease needs to be removed with a solvent. If the correct brush cannot be obtained it is usually possible to adapt one from another application, but do use something intended for similar use. There are many grades of carbon and other materials used for brushes—the wrong one would wear rapidly and could damage the commutator or not conduct the current as well as it might.

Brushes are usually fitted near the end of the dynamo assembly, but this is no problem as long as there is access. The job is more awkward when the body lacks windows, in which case the brushes need to be entered into their holders with the spring against the brush side.

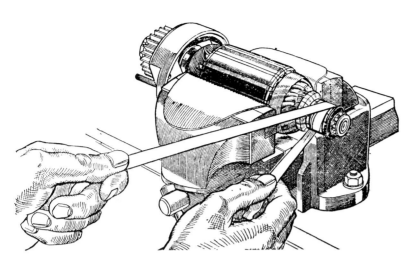

Cleaning up the dynamo commutator with fine glass paper, after which it will need a good clean

The end plate and armature can then be assembled, after which the brush can be worked into position with the spring holding it correctly.

The bearings may be ball races or bushes and either can be a problem to change and set up. Ball races may need heat to remove them from their housing but this must not be allowed to get too near to the electrics. The inner race may be a tight fit on the armature, requiring a special tool to draw it off. Be equally careful when pushing the new one on to avoid pressing on the outer, which could cause the balls to indent the track.

Also look out for oil seals which may need to be changed, additional locking rings calling for special spanners or delicate work with a pin punch, and any need to shim the races to control end float. Any of these conditions needs to be treated with care.

Bushes are usually sintered bronze and need to be immersed in a light oil for 24 hours before being pressed into place with a mandrel of the same diameter as the armature shaft. Bush lubrication in use requires a few drops of thin machine oil every 1000 miles. The ball race or races should be pre-packed with a high-melting-point grease, but do not use too much or it will fly everywhere.

The commutator needs to be clean, round, smooth and with the mica insulators between the segments undercut. Cleaning can be done with a soft rag and methylated spirits or, if really black, with fine glass paper. This is best wrapped around the commutator and worked diabolo fashion with a length of tape. It must then be thoroughly washed.

If the commutator is worn or not running true, it will need to be skimmed in a lathe. This must be done with a very sharp tool and the result has to be true to the armature shaft. It may then be necessary to cut back the mica insulation to compensate for the reduction in diameter, which can be done using a hacksaw blade ground to suit the width.

The requirement is that all the mica is taken down about 0.02 in. below the commutator surface and square to it. Thus half-round or vee grooves are no good, and neither is a cut that is narrower than the mica. It is a fiddly job and has to be done without scratching the surface that the brushes bear against. You will need a fine Swiss file with which to de-burr the slots, and then a final polish with the glass paper followed by a wash in meths.

The rest of the parts simply need checking over for damage or wear, and should be repaired as necessary. Inspect all the wires and leads, and check that they have no stray strands that could cause trouble. If the dynamo has a cover band, make sure that it fits correctly and that its insulation is in good order and doing its job. Inspect the clamp screw and nut as these often suffer careless handling.

Part of the dynamo circuit is its earth connection to ground, and this is as important as any other. It follows that, where it is clamped to a magneto, the body must be free from dirt, grease or paint, there must be no burrs to affect the fit, and the clamping strap must be tight. Dirt between the two instruments will also cause the drive to be noisy.

Armature checking

First check and repair the thread at the driving end if this has suffered at all. Then move on

to the keyway and shaft that the drive gear or sprocket has to fit to. If badly worn, Loctite Quick Metal could be an answer to return the assembly to its original rigidity.

There are two electrical tests that can be done with a meter or battery and bulb. The first is to check between the armature and each commutator segment. There should be no connection—if there is one, it means that there is a short-circuit from the winding to earth. Test two is between adjacent commutator segments and these should be joined with a small resistance. This comes from the coil wired between them—if a larger resistance is recorded, it means the coil is broken and the current has to run round all the others to make the connection.

In either case the armature will need rewinding, which is a specialist job. This may also apply if there is any sign of heat, dry joints or stray pieces of solder around the join of the winding to the commutator segment. It is possible for the joints to break so check for this with a magnifying glass. Repairs can be made but will call for a good soldering iron of at least 100 watts of power. With care, the part can be reclaimed.

Field coil

There are two checks that can be made. One is to make sure the coil is not shorting to the case and that there is no doubt as to its insulation. The second is a continuity check to make sure the two ends are joined to one another.

The coil resistance is only about 3 ohms, so you will need a good meter to measure this and detect if the coil has shorted internally.

Should the coil be inoperative, it will need changing, which is not the easiest of jobs. It is held in place by one or two large screws that are done up very tightly and then caulked by punching the case metal into their slots. The first step is to drill this away. Next, it is necessary to devise a screwdriver that can be held in the screw slot and turned with enough force. The driver bit may come from a socket spanner

LEFT Checking out the dynamo armature with battery and meter, which is a professional Avo—and nice if you have one

RIGHT Checking the dynamo field coil

set, but the rest of the arrangement will have to be contrived.

This should undo the screws, but you are not yet out of the woods. The pole shoe and field coil can be removed and the coil changed, but this leaves the problem of refitting the parts. The pole shoe must fit hard against the dynamo body or it will not clear the armature. To do this, an expander is used—while it is in place, the fixing screws are done up tight.

It is then worth assembling the armature and ends to the body to make sure the parts can turn without touching.

Lucas dynamo

The earliest type had three brushes, with two opposing and one at right angles to the other. This gave a degree of control to the output, and the third and one other brush were joined to earth. The remaining brush connected via the cut-out to the control switch, and from there to the battery. The dynamo shunt, or field coil, was connected to the same brush, and its other end went to the switch. It went to earth via this, but the switch positions included a half-charge one, which added a resistance into the line.

This was the E3 available in dynamo and Mag-dyno forms. It was superseded by another third-brush type, in which this brush could be moved relative to the others to regulate the output. It was still not a very precise arrangement

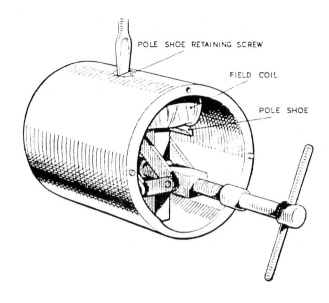

POLE SHOE RETAINING SCREW

FIELD COIL

POLE SHOE

ABOVE **Fitting a new field coil using an expander to locate it firmly into place**

BELOW **The Lucas dynamo with added distributor for a multi-cylinder machine**

and in most cases a half-charge resistance continued to be fitted. The field coil connected to the third brush and to earth via the switch or the resistor. One of the main brushes went to earth and the other to the battery via the cut-out. This was usually built into the end of the unit, though not always. Third-brush dynamos must not be run with the battery out of circuit or disconnected. If this is done, the voltage produced will rise too far and may damage both bulbs and field windings.

The basic dynamo was made in various forms to suit the drive method and whether the dynamo was mounted by itself or to a magneto. A further type had ignition contact points at the end of the armature and was used when the machine had coil ignition. Types with a movable third brush and built-in cut-out were the E3B, E3D and E3MD. Where the third brush was fixed, but not at right angles as in the original type, the models were the E3C and E3M, while if the cut-out was removed for remote mounting the dynamo became the E3A or E3E.

MOTOR CYCLE DYNAMO MODEL C35SD

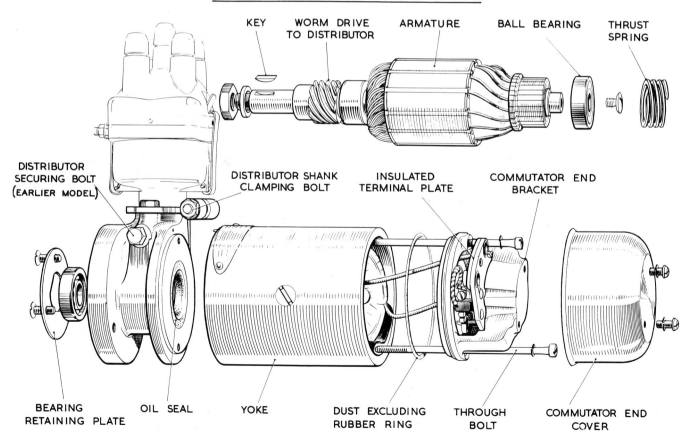

KEY

WORM DRIVE TO DISTRIBUTOR

ARMATURE

BALL BEARING

THRUST SPRING

DISTRIBUTOR SECURING BOLT (EARLIER MODEL)

DISTRIBUTOR SHANK CLAMPING BOLT

INSULATED TERMINAL PLATE

COMMUTATOR END BRACKET

BEARING RETAINING PLATE

OIL SEAL

YOKE

DUST EXCLUDING RUBBER RING

THROUGH BOLT

COMMUTATOR END COVER

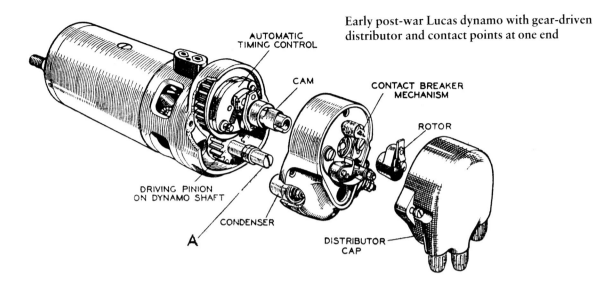

AUTOMATIC
TIMING CONTROL

CAM

CONTACT BREAKER
MECHANISM

ROTOR

DRIVING PINION
ON DYNAMO SHAFT

CONDENSER

A

DISTRIBUTOR
CAP

Early post-war Lucas dynamo with gear-driven distributor and contact points at one end

By modifying the wiring and fitting a cvc control unit, any of these third-brush dynamos can be converted to a two-brush form. In this case, all connections must be secure and well out of any danger of accidental shorting to earth.

In 1936 Lucas introduced the cvc and a two-brush dynamo that remained an industry standard until the alternator took over. The dynamo wiring became extremely simple with one brush and one end of the field coil connected to earth, while the other brush and coil end went to the cvc via separate connections.

The basic models were the 35-watt E3H and E3HM which had 3 in. diameter bodies, the latter being the unit that formed part of the Mag-dyno. Construction of both was straightforward, with access to the brushes via a cover band and the armature supported by a bush and a ball race.

The field resistance of these units is 3.2 ohms. If a suitable meter is not to hand, connect a 6-volt battery across the coil with an ammeter in series. The reading should be approximately 1.9 amps.

AMC favoured a version listed as the E3AR on their singles, for they chose to drive their dynamo by chain from the crankshaft. They were not loved for this, nor for the location of the dynamo in the engine plates just above the gearbox. It was worse on a Matchless as the magneto sat above it and not ahead of the cylinder as on an AJS; it was moved for 1952. A further version of the dynamo was the E3KA2 which included a contact-breaker,

automatic advance mechanism and distributor. The ignition components were gear driven from the brush end of the armature to run at half engine speed.

Another form was the 40-watt MC45, used by the post-war Sunbeam twin on the front end of its crankcase, and also the Scott two-stroke twin, fixed to the crankcase door. This was shorter and fatter than the others to suit its installation and had its connections on top of the body.

For 1949 Lucas lengthened their dynamos to increase the output to 60 watts in line with

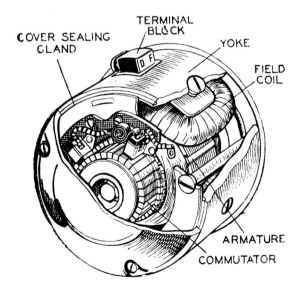

COVER SEALING
GLAND

TERMINAL
BLOCK

YOKE

FIELD
COIL

ARMATURE

COMMUTATOR

The Lucas pancake dynamo fitted to in-line machines such as the post-war Sunbeam

71

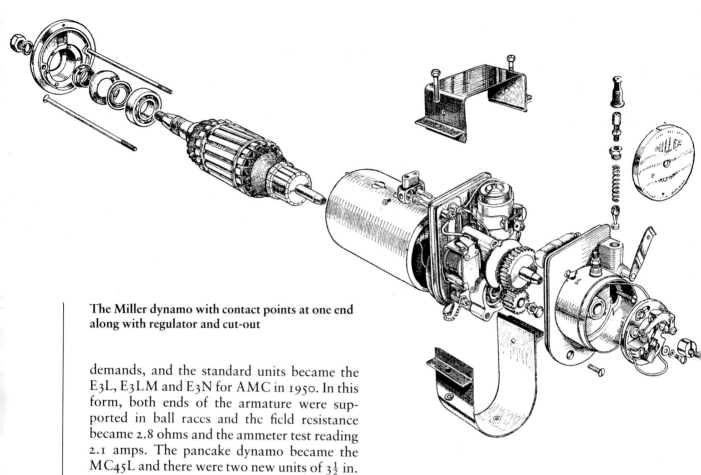

The Miller dynamo with contact points at one end along with regulator and cut-out

demands, and the standard units became the E3L, E3LM and E3N for AMC in 1950. In this form, both ends of the armature were supported in ball races and the field resistance became 2.8 ohms and the ammeter test reading 2.1 amps. The pancake dynamo became the MC45L and there were two new units of $3\frac{1}{2}$ in. diameter and higher output.

These were the 75-watt C35S and C35SD, which were intended for machines with coil ignition. The first was the basic unit, but the second included a distributor and contact-breaker assembly driven by skew gears from the armature. This type was used on the Royal Enfield twin, new for 1949, and the Ariel Square Four which was revamped for that year. The cam and distributor were to suit the number of cylinders, and the new unit replaced a hard-pressed magneto on the four which had been running at engine speed and feeding a dynamo-driven distributor.

In 1952 the E3 dynamo went out of production while the E3L continued, and for 1957 the latter had a new end cover. This was held by a single screw and the wires were taken through a moulding to an inside terminal plate. At the same time, the driven end was smoothed out with a die-cast cover.

In these forms the Lucas dynamos continued until their need disappeared, either because of a change to an alternator or due to the end of a model line.

Miller dynamo

This firm's equipment was fitted as standard to many Velocette and Vincent models and followed a similar path to Lucas. In fact, Vincent offered a kit to allow the Lucas to be fitted on many models and it is common practice to fit a Lucas cvc in place of the Miller regulator and cut-out.

The Miller cut-out was fitted on the end of the dynamo but in other respects construction was much the same for both makes, and the same procedures and techniques should produce the required results. Perhaps the most noticeable difference was that in the two-brush design the field resistance was fitted into the dynamo body along with the field coil. Thus, there are four wires emerging from the interior even if two of them are joined. This junction is one of the leads to the regulator, while the other end of the field coil is earthed and the resistor, value 7 ohms, connects to the positive brush.

Due to the resistance, plus the cut-out in most cases, the end plate has many brass strips and connections, screws and washers. All of these need to be very carefully checked over and noted before they are touched. It is very easy indeed to assemble an insulating washer on the wrong side of a strip or wire and produce a disaster. Check with a meter, before and after, against the circuit and make sure it all corresponds.

The three-brush Miller with cut-out is the DM3G, which was replaced by a two-brush DVR at about 1937. This had the regulator box mounted on the dynamo body in many cases, although this was not essential. It retained the cut-out on the brush plate at the end of the dynamo.

The early dynamo could be mounted with the magneto to form the Miller Dyno-Mag ('Mag-dyno' being a Lucas trademark) and was chain driven. It could be released by slackening the strap and turning the body which removed the chain tension. The cut-out was usually mounted separately in this case.

Vincents fitted the $3\frac{1}{2}$ in. diameter D9S on most of the B series but changed to the 50-watt, 3 in. D6 for the C series. These were two-brush types with the cut-out part of the dynamo.

In the late 1930s, the 30-watt DH1 was fitted to some Royal Enfield models and ran at engine speed. It had a half-speed contact-breaker at the brush end, and the cut-out and control unit were housed on top of the assembly. Only the ignition coil was mounted separately. Post-war, this was joined by the longer DH3 which produced 50 watts like the basic D6. It was revised for 1949, with the control unit and cut-out mounted on the brush plate inboard of the gear-driven contact points, which had manual advance.

These varieties continued and for 1950 the firm offered the DH1 and DH3 with half-speed contact-breaker, the DM3G1 which had the points cam running at dynamo speed, and two basic dynamos. These last were the 36-watt, 3 in. diameter DVR, the same-size 50-watt D6, and the 50-watt, $3\frac{1}{2}$ in. DGS. By 1952 the list was down to four, with the two DH models, the DVR and the D6.

For 1953 this last was replaced by the DM3 which had third-brush control, but as the decade progressed the dynamos were used less and less. Vincent changed to Lucas on the D models of 1954, but Velocette kept to Miller until 1966—some of the last ones fitted were controlled by a Lucas cvc.

BTH dynamo

This was a rare item found on the LE Velocette in its early days, as from the middle of 1951 (at engine 12640) a Miller generator began to be fitted. From late 1953 only Miller systems were used, although the BTH remained on the lists until 1956.

The 35-watt BTH dynamo was short and fat to suit its installation but was otherwise much as any two-brush dynamo. The cut-out was built into the housing, along with all the ignition components, and the output was switch controlled.

Repair and renovation follow the same lines as for other dynamos with attention to the brushes, commutator and detail part condition. The whole assembly was known as the type PEC.

Pre-war, BTH produced a Mag-Generator which combined a dynamo with a magneto. This was fitted to some early Vincent HRD 500 cc engines prior to 1937. Straps hold the two together and they may also appear on JAP or Rudge Python engines of that era.

Even older was the BTH Sparklight, which took current from the magneto primary via a brush and collecting segment. This aided the battery in keeping the lights going, being a forerunner of the ML and Lucas Maglita design. The device dated from around 1920 and did not survive for too long.

Siba dynamo

This German unit is usually found on two-stroke engines, since it combines both dynamo and starter in one unit known as a Dynastart. The two functions are obtained by having coils and brushes for each purpose and a suitable control box. Four sizes were offered with outputs ranging from 60–120 watts, and a contact points plate was part of the assembly. The ignition cam for this could be driven directly or via an advance mechanism, while it was possible to connect the starter side to run the engine in reverse. This function was needed for some bubble-cars with two-stroke engines to allow them to be reversed. Many applications of this type, and for scooters, had a cooling fan attached to the stator.

Maintenance is mainly concerned with cleaning the brushes and commutator, and the design differs from others in that the rotor

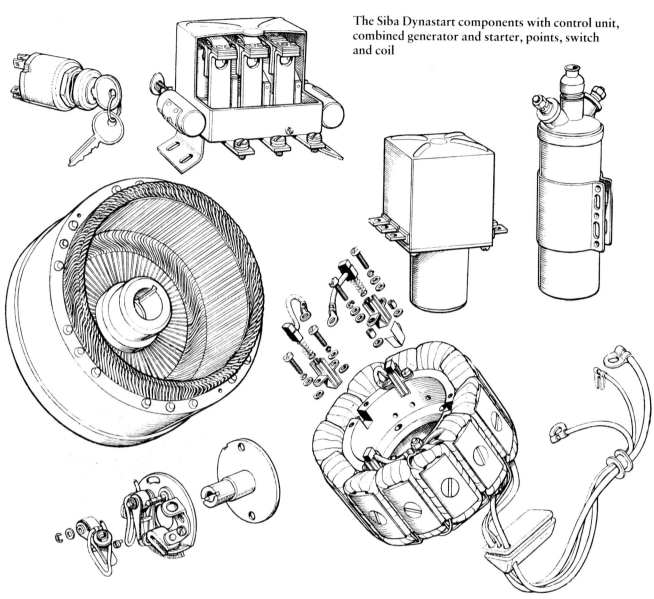

The Siba Dynastart components with control unit, combined generator and starter, points, switch and coil

windings surround the stator coils and have a disc commutator with axial brushes pressed against it. The rotor requires a special puller to remove it and the commutator can be skimmed back to a depth of not more than 0.08 in. The insulation will then need undercutting to a depth of 0.02–0.03 in.

The brushes have wear grooves halfway along them and should be replaced if worn to anything near these. The contact points also warrant checking and the gap for the original types was 0.014–0.016 in. Later cams with a '/1' suffix to their numbers required the gap to be 0.020–0.022 in.

The air gap on a Siba is 0.008 in., so it is most important that all parts are perfectly clean, that the rotor fits the crankshaft properly and runs true, and that it and the stator are mounted concentrically. All these points are well worth checking.

Maglita

Mention should be made again of this combined-duty instrument. Its construction is much as for other magnetos, and there are two magnets within which should be bridged by an iron keeper before the armature is removed.

The cut-out in this must have clean contacts fitted securely in their blades, while the operating arm must be free from oil or dust and quite free to move on its pin.

The armature windings can be tested with a meter, or battery and bulb, noting that the design provides for only two of the four commutator segments being in circuit. Check for broken connections or dry joints where the windings are soldered to the segments.

12-volt dynamo

A change to 12 volts can be beneficial in that more power becomes available for the lights and other systems, bulbs are easier to obtain, and the system will work more efficiently.

It may be claimed that this can be done by simply fitting a 12-volt cvc from a car in place of the existing unit. This may work but there are snags, one being the problem of locating a cvc in reasonable condition. If it is not in good condition, it will need renovating in the same manner as the motorcycle one and for this you will need the equivalent car book. The next snag is that you still have an electro-mechanical unit susceptible to vibration and weather, so you will not have progressed very far.

The final and most important problem is that the car unit will regulate as for a car dynamo and may subject the field coil to an excess current so that it burns out. Where a car unit has been used without this occurring, it will be either due to not being too heavily loaded or because its settings provide the limitation.

The real answer is an electronic unit which replaces the cvc and allows for 12 volts while limiting the field current to an acceptable level. The same unit is also available in 6-volt form for owners who wish to keep to this but want it under better control.

The units were originally designed to suit Lucas dynamos but can deal with most others. A variation is offered for the Miller which replaces the rather difficult regulator used by that dynamo, but all types are likely to reduce the dynamo life to some extent.

For anyone using their machine for general use on today's roads, this change is well worth undertaking as it will allow the use of a much better headlamp. At the other end of the machine, a modern stop and tail lamp can be added which might not be original but really is an essential in modern traffic. Keep the old parts for shows or rallies.

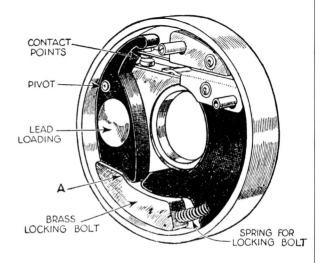

The **Maglita** cut-out in which the parts need to be polished so they all move easily

CHAPTER 8
The regulator

The regulator is also known as the compensated-voltage control unit, or cvc, and on the motorcycle is mounted with the cut-out in a small box. It was first offered by Lucas at about 1936 and went with their two-brush dynamo from then onwards in various, similar forms. The unit has two coils, one for each job, under its cover, unlike car units which have three. In the case of cars, cvc stands for current-voltage regulator.

Miller dynamos were either regulated with a third brush or a regulator of their own design, the cut-out remaining on the dynamo end bracket.

Regulator function

This is needed to control the output of the dynamo, which rises with its speed. This is most easily done by placing a resistance in series with the field winding to reduce its current and hence the magnetic field and the dynamo output.

With the third-brush system, the brush provided some degree of control as the speed rose, but did not take into account the state of the battery or its load. Thus, the half-charge switch position was provided so the rider could reduce the charge in the summer and increase it for the winter loads.

The regulator replaced this crude system with an automatic one, though still based on adding a resistor in series with the field coil. Spring-loaded contacts are placed across this component, so when it is closed, it is bypassed and the output rises. This increases the output

which is fed into a winding whose magnetic pull opens the contacts, so the resistor comes into effect again and reduces the output.

Thus, the contacts are in a constant state of vibration, just like a domestic bell, to control the output. The system is further refined by the use of twin windings to control the contacts, and the effects take into account the battery voltage and load.

Cut-out function

This acts as an automatic switch between the dynamo and battery to stop the latter trying to motor the former when the engine is not running. Without it, the dynamo could be burnt

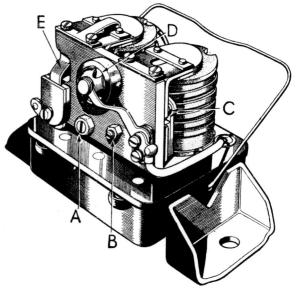

The Lucas MCR2 regulator with carbon-disc control resistor and FADE terminal line-up

out in its attempt to be a starter motor.

The unit comprises another pair of contacts with twin windings to magnetically close them. A shunt winding of fine wire is connected across the dynamo brushes and produces enough pull to overcome the contact-spring tension when the dynamo is generating. The points are in the main line from the dynamo and a heavy-gauge series winding then takes the current on to the battery and helps to hold the contacts firmly together.

When the dynamo has slowed nearly to a stop, the current flow in the series winding reverses as the battery tries to supply the dynamo and make it work as a motor. This reverses the magnetic flux to help the spring part the contacts.

Regulator servicing

This is not something to be lightly undertaken as it is easy to disturb the settings and create a situation where either the battery is never properly charged, or it or the dynamo and regulator are damaged. However, correctly approached, the unit can be checked and set up without too much trouble.

You must have the correct instruments to take electrical measurements to the required degree of accuracy. Most of the rest of the work comprises mechanical setting of gaps using feeler gauges once the assembly has been cleaned and inspected.

The first step in all cases is to establish the circuit diagram of the dynamo and regulator together, the wiring diagram of both including all internal connections, and the physical layout of the two items. All three can be totally dissimilar and it is this which gives many owners problems. This is not helped by Lucas using an internal frame as part of the circuit to which several leads join. Despite its appearance, it is not the earth line but the main feed from the dynamo and must be insulated as such.

Trace out the circuit of the cvc and work out how it all fits into the circuit diagram and what happens when the contacts open or close. Remember that the cvc is a delicate electromechanical unit and treat it accordingly.

Lucas regulators

The original was the MCR1 which was fitted

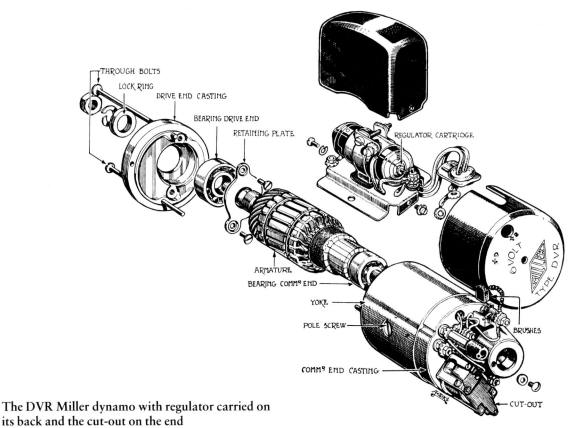

The DVR Miller dynamo with regulator carried on its back and the cut-out on the end

with a wire-wound resistor of 27–33 ohms. For the 1950s it was replaced by the MCR2, which had a round carbon-disc resistor of 36–45 ohms mounted on the back of the internal frame. To accommodate this the cover gained a swelling, but otherwise the two units are really the same. Both have their terminal connections letter coded in the order FADE.

This was changed to FAED for the RB107 of 1954 and reversed to DEAF for the RB108 of 1960. A special regulator marked NiFe was used when a nickel-iron battery was fitted. This was necessary to suit this form of battery, although the standard cvc could be used temporarily. All these units follow a similar pattern of checking and cleaning, with replacement of the contacts if necessary. Whether replaced or just cleaned, the unit will need setting mechanically and then electrically.

MCR units

The first step in setting the MCR1 regulator concerns the air gap between the vertical leg of the armature that carries the contact and the frame. This is set by placing a 0.015 in. feeler in this air gap and, with the two fixing screws slack, holding the armature against this gauge and down on to the top of the bobbin core. Lock the screw and then check the air gap between the top of the bobbin core and the horizontal leg of the armature, but not under the stop rivet. This should be 0.020–0.025 in. and is adjusted with shims at the back of the fixed contact. Once all this is done, the gap

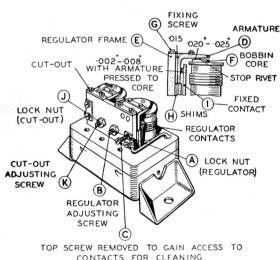

TOP SCREW REMOVED TO GAIN ACCESS TO CONTACTS FOR CLEANING

The Lucas MCR1 and its setting details as given in a BSA service sheet

between the contacts when the armature is pressed down to the bobbin core should be 0.002–0.008 in.

On the MCR2 the procedure is much the same, but the air gap between the armature and frame is 0.020 in. This can taper either way down to 0.018 in. The bobbin-core face to armature air gap should be 0.012–0.020 in. with the gauge placed beneath the brass pip or shim. The contacts gap with the armature on the core should be 0.006–0.017 in. and is adjusted by bending the fixed contact carrier.

The electrical settings are carried out on the machine and commence with a piece of card placed between the cut-out contacts. Disconnect the lead from terminal A and connect a 10-volt meter between D and E. Run the engine until the meter flicks and then steadies, but avoid high speeds as the open-circuit voltage could be excessive. Read the meter, which at 20 degrees Celsius should be 7.8–8.2 volts, but for every 10 degrees Celsius rise in temperature deduct 0.2 volts, and for a fall add 0.2 volts.

If required, adjust the voltage with the screw in the frame and turn it clockwise to raise the setting. Then run the dynamo at about 4500 rpm and check the voltage which should be 8.9 volts at a temperature of 20 degrees Celsius. Carry out these checks quickly or errors can occur due to a voltage build-up. The MCR2 is tested in the same way but the first figure is then 8.0–8.4 volts at 20 degrees Celsius.

The cut-out setting of the MCR1 is checked electrically with the voltmeter between D and E. Run the engine up until the cut-out contacts close, at which point the voltage should be 6.2–6.6 volts. Adjust if necessary with the screw in the frame, which turns clockwise to raise the setting.

Then disconnect the lead from A and connect the voltmeter between A and E. Run the engine up and then let the revs drop until the cut-out contacts open. At this point the voltage should be 3.5–5.3 volts.

On the MCR2 there are mechanical settings, with the vertical air gap between the frame and the armature set at 0.014 in. and the bobbin-core face to armature set at 0.011–0.015 in. These gaps should then be held by gauges and the armature pressed against them, at which point the air gap between the armature and the stop plate arm should be 0.030–0.034 in. This is adjusted by bending it. Finally, with a 0.025 in. gauge between the armature and the bobbin-core face, the contact gap should be 0.002–0.006 in., which is adjusted by bending the fixed contact bracket.

The electrical tests are as for the MCR1, but the cut-in voltage should be 6.3–6.7 volts and the cut-out 4.8–5.5 volts. This unit can be further checked with an ammeter in the lead between dynamo D and cvc D. It should show a charge when the cut-out points close and when the engine stops, and a discharge of 3–5 amps when the contacts open.

RB units

These have a different method for setting and the regulator adjustment starts by slackening the armature screws. A 0.021 in. gauge then goes between the bobbin-core face and the armature which should be held squarely against it while the screws are tightened.

Hold the armature on this gauge and then adjust the fixed contact above it until it just touches the moving one on the top of the armature. Then tighten its lock nut.

The electrical check again calls for a card between the cut-out points and the disconnection of the lead to terminal A. Connect a voltmeter between D and E, and run the engine slowly up to a dynamo speed of 3000 rpm. The voltage should be 8.0–8.4 volts at 20 degrees Celsius, with a rise of 0.2 volts for every 10 degrees Celsius drop in temperature and a fall of the same amount if it gets warmer.

Adjustment of this value is by means of the screw in the back of the frame below the car-

Lucas RB108 regulator and a zener diode shown with an old penny for comparison

bon resistor. It is turned clockwise to raise the setting. Lock the screw, then allow the dynamo to slow right down and then run it up to 4500 rpm and note the reading which should not exceed 8.9 volts at 20 degrees Celsius.

Do all these tests quickly or the readings will be in error due to a build-up of heat in the shunt winding. Do not overspeed the dynamo or the high voltage built up will result in a false setting, and make quite sure the cvc is properly earthed or this work will be inaccurate and in vain.

The cut-out is set by first pressing the armature down on to the bobbin-core face and then checking the gap between the armature tongue and its stop arm. The first of these is the extension that rises above the armature and carries a contact; the second is the fixed plate above this. The gap should be 0.025–0.040 in. and is adjusted by bending the stop arm.

With this set, again press the armature to the bobbin-core face and check that the fixed contact blade is deflected by 0.010–0.020 in., thus ensuring that the contacts are making a good electrical connection. The setting is adjusted by moving the fixed blade, as the moving one has to relate to the stop arm.

The electrical tests for the RB107 and RB108 cut-out are as for the MCR2, and the same cut-in and cut-out voltages apply. Adjustment is by the screw in the back of the frame.

Lucas cvc notes

A machine with an E3 dynamo should have an MCR1 cvc but can be run with the MCR2 listed under part number 37144A.

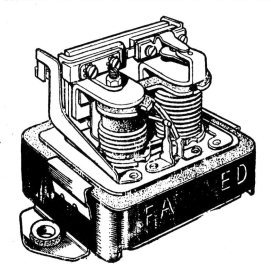

The RB107 Lucas regulator with revised terminals and interior settings

Miller spares in the form of a cut-out to the left and regulator to the right

You can use the machine with the battery removed as long as the cvc is working as it should. The main lead from the battery must be insulated and kept well clear of the frame if you do this. Do not fit a lower-voltage battery as the regulator will then spend its time trying to uprate it and may weld its contacts together in the process. If the battery is in the circuit, it must be kept topped up or the cvc is fooled into feeding it excess current which could easily ruin the battery, dynamo and cvc.

If the dynamo polarity has reversed, simply hold the cut-out contacts together for a few seconds and then pull them apart.

The direction of rotation for the dynamo can be reversed by switching over the field coil wires on a two-brush type, but for a three-brush dynamo a mirror image is required to place the control brush in its optimum position.

Make sure that the dynamo and cvc are connected correctly between the D and F terminals. Both sets of wires are held by non-reversible plates but a check could save a lot of trouble. Use a meter on the machine wiring as it may run out of sight and could have been crossed over or shorted to earth at some time.

Miller regulator

This may be mounted separately from the dynamo or mounted with it. In either case the same assembly is used, which is more sophisticated than the Lucas in that it has three conditions and two sets of points. The cut-out remains as a separate unit.

In fact, the Miller regulator would seem to have been too clever for its own good and thus tricky to set up and rather prone to going out of adjustment. In the main it functions as the Lucas by inserting a 7-ohm resistor in series with the field coil to reduce the output. It then follows the usual path of less output, contacts close to short-out the resistor, while with more output, contacts open, and so on.

The difficulty comes from a second pair of contacts fitted in the unit and linked to the first. Thus, the pair across the field resistor are normally closed, while the others which short across the field coil are open. The next position has both sets of contacts open so that both resistor and field coil are in series to reduce the output. Stage three closes the second pair of points to leave the resistor in circuit and the field coil shorted. Outputs from the dynamo in these three conditions are full charge, half charge and no charge.

The regulator is constructed with a winding on an iron body held between two plates, Inside this is an iron core which can move axially and it has a contact screwed into each end. It is connected to the junction between field coil and resistor in the dynamo.

Each end plate also carries a contact so the core can move between them to make a connection with one or the other, or neither, to create the three stages. At one end is a red insulator plate which has an outer live plate connected to the D terminal and positive brush of the dynamo.

The outer end is more complex and includes a spring which normally holds the first pair of contacts closed, at the red plate end. The end plate is longer and threaded for an adjuster to load the spring and a carrier for the contact. Both end-plate contacts can be adjusted in or out, as well as the spring whose adjuster is

locked by a grub screw in the periphery of the end plate.

The internal winding connects across the dynamo brushes and so is wired across the end plates which achieve this effect.

The main adjustment is done on the spring but if the device has been stripped the contacts will need to be set. This is started with the earthed end contact holder removed. The red end contact then goes in as far as possible, and then out $1\frac{1}{2}$ turns before it is locked.

The unit is then connected and the dynamo run fairly slowly. The spring load should be adjusted so the output is 7.5–7.9 volts and then locked with its grub screw. The second contact holder is then fitted and the contact gently screwed in as far as possible. This will close both contacts, hence the need for care, and a test meter across the ends will show no resistance. The contact is then backed off half a turn and locked. The voltage check should then be repeated.

The Siba control unit with its three coils and the circuit diagram for them

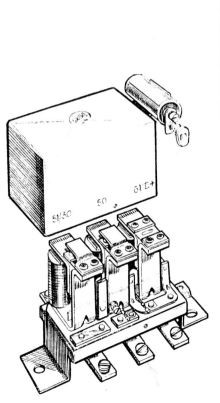

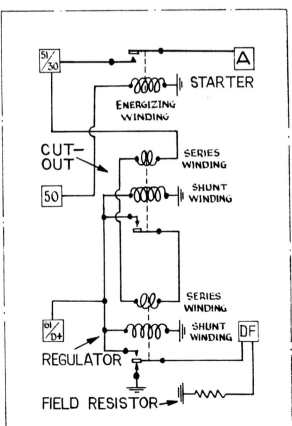

Do not fiddle with the contacts as it is easy to damage the regulator. If you must do so, undoing the contact at the end about a quarter of a turn will reduce the output voltage, while undoing the earth end will increase it. The latter adjustment can be up to two turns but monitor the voltage if you try any of this. The regulator may benefit from rubber mounting to protect it from engine vibration, but if this is done, do not forget that the case has to be earthed.

If the regulator is left off the machine, the half-charge condition prevails and can be used as a temporary expedient. If the regulator leads were then joined, a full-charge condition would occur, followed in due course by a burnt-out field winding or solder flying off the commutator.

Miller cut-out

This is normally mounted on the end of the dynamo and is the same as the Lucas electrically. The resistance of the series winding should be 0.09–0.10 ohms and the resistance of the shunt winding 55–56 ohms.

The points should close at 6 volts when a current of up to 0.25 amps is being generated, and their gap should be $\frac{1}{32}$ in.

Miller with Lucas

As the Miller regulator is so hard to adjust, it has become common practice to regulate a Miller dynamo with a Lucas cvc. This can be done with either a two- or three-brush type, and the Lucas part replaces the cut-out as well.

In the main, the work consists of removing parts and connections from the dynamo to leave one end of the field coil joined to the earthed brush, and the other brush and field-coil end connected to D and F at the cvc.

The resistance in the Miller dynamo no longer needs to be connected and the various connecting strips of brass can mainly be removed. The cut-out goes altogether, which gives more room for any terminal block that may be needed.

This arrangement was fitted as standard on Velocette singles for 1965–66 before the firm turned over to a complete Lucas system.

Siba control unit

This differs from the Lucas as it has three coils in it for regulator, cut-out and starter. The first two operate in precisely the same way, and the third is a simple relay to connect the battery to the starter windings.

The cut-out is the only adjustable item in the box and should work at 11.5–12.5 volts across the terminals 61/D + and earth.

CHAPTER 9
Alternator systems

The alternator had a considerable appeal when it first appeared as it dispensed with all the tiresome business of brushes, commutator and drive systems. In truth, it was no different from the flywheel-magneto system used by two-strokes for many years and, like them, was easy to mount on crankshaft and case.

The snag was one of control, for the greater output demanded by larger machines ruled out the simple arrangements used by two-strokes. The principles of rectification to change the alternating current of the alternator into direct current suitable for the battery were well known many years ago, but the materials to do the job were not then available.

Early Villiers engines had a simple two-segment commutator to deal with the problem, but around 1930 they introduced a true alternator with a Westinghouse metal plate rectifier. There were a good few strictures to go with this advance and the user was enjoined never to dismantle the rectifier, and to pull out the alternator connections should the battery be disconnected.

The power provided was minimal and the headlamp bulb only 6 watts, while the pilot and tail were down to 1.8 watts. These problems of low power and massive rectifier size were to remain until the post-war years and developments in semi-conductors.

As early as 1946, Lucas had an alternator with two coils and a six-pole rotor connected to a smaller rectifier. However, another problem began to appear in the form of overcharging. It was dealt with by a relay which fed excess current into a resistor for dissipation when not needed, but foretold a difficulty that was to plague the system for two decades.

Over the years, the rectifier changed from coated metal to selenium and then silicon diodes which could deal with far greater outputs. The control problem remained and was dealt with by switching the alternator coils into circuit as their output was called for. As this was for the lights, this meant that the light switch had to be wired into the generating circuit.

The Lucas RM18 alternator with its six coils and circular frame

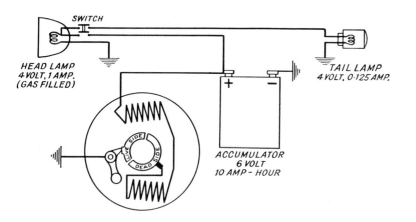

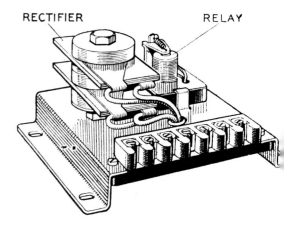

Crude two-piece commutator used with alternator in early days to charge battery

Early post-war rectifier and relay which could only deal with very limited outputs

A further complication arose when the machine had coil ignition, as it was required that when the battery was flat, most or all of the output should go straight to the ignition side to enable the engine to be started. This introduced further wiring complications and the need for a three-position ignition switch to provide off, on and emergency.

These problems were finally solved by a move to 12-volt systems and control by a zener diode which could respond to the system's needs. This resulted in better control and a much simpler wiring loom.

Alternator servicing

The alternator requires no maintenance but can bear an occasional inspection. As it usually lives in the chaincase, the oil in this should be changed at regular intervals in case it becomes contaminated and deposits any metal particles on the rotor or stator.

If dismantled, the parts should be cleaned of any debris they have attracted, but no magnet keeper is required. Check that the output connectors are in good condition.

Both stator and rotor can be repaired in most cases and anything unknown should be looked over with care. On the stator, the first checks should be on the wiring of the coils to see if all are insulated from the laminations. Next, inspect the join between the output cables and the coil wires, and follow this by tracing the way these are connected.

There are several variations on this which also affect the number of leads, which range

between two and five. Draw the circuit out and note the wire colours if these can still be distinguished. Early Lucas alternators had three leads which began as light, mid and dark green, but aged so they all became more or less the same. With your circuit diagram this will no longer be a problem.

Next check that the coils are mechanically secure on their poles and deal with any trouble in this area. Inspect the pole ends to see if the rotor has been touching them at any time and also make sure that the stator is a good fit on to its mounting spigot.

The rotor should be a good fit on the shaft, whether this is a parallel or taper fit, and its location key must be in good order. Check the periphery in case it has been touching the stator poles. If this has been happening, file the poles back to give a minimum 0.008 in. and general 0.012 in. clearance all the way round. Also check that the rotor is not running out of true, as this would affect the gap.

Sometimes the rotor centre comes loose inside the assembly and makes the engine sound as if the mains or big-ends have gone. A repair can be done by machining enough of the alloy side away to allow the core to be removed. It can then be refitted using a Loctite gap filler and once set should remain a solid lump from then on.

The remaining checks that can be done are electrical and carried out with the alternator assembled to the machine. Most call for an accurate voltmeter and a load resistor of only 1 ohm. This has to be accurate or the correct test results will not be obtained.

The 1-ohm test resistor

This has to be capable of carrying 10 amps without overheating and can be made from about four yards of 18 swg (0.048 in.) diameter Nichrome wire, suitably calibrated using an ammeter and voltmeter. The process makes use of the equation that voltage equals current multiplied by the resistance, so if this last is 1 ohm then volts and amps will be the same.

The wire is bent into two and this bend connects to a 6-volt battery which has a voltmeter across its terminals. An ammeter connects to the second battery terminal and a lead is taken from it to a clip. This connects to the two wire ends and is moved along, making contact with both. When the volts and amps readings are the same, the wire resistance is 1 ohm and it can be cut at that point. It should then be wound on a hollow, non-metallic former of about 2 in. diameter.

A similar process can produce other ohmic values.

Lucas alternators

The first production unit was the IA45, which went primarily on BSA Bantams for 1950–53 but was also used by the Indian Brave, Dot and OEC. It offered emergency starting or direct lighting as well as its more usual battery supply.

The unit differed from all the others in only having two coils, one of which had a centre tapping, and a contact-breaker at its outboard end. The cam went on the end of the rotor and could have an advance mechanism or not. For the later Bantams, the contact plate carried an extra bearing to support the shaft and ensure true running for the cam. There was also an IA55 which generated 10 watts more, but was not equipped with the contact points.

The IA45 differs from later units in that the rotor should *not* be removed from the stator or magnetism will be lost. In use, a half-charge resistance of 6.5 ohms was included in the circuit.

The first of the major run of Lucas alternators appeared in the middle of 1951 and was called the RM12. It set a pattern that all the others followed, with a plain rotor and a six-pole stator which was built up from iron laminations.

The RM12 stator was hexagonal in form with a turned spigot diameter machined on to the corners. It produced 55 watts and was used in three forms on Triumph twins for 1952–53. The original A type had four leads but the others had six, and all the B ones were converted to C as far as possible.

The dimensions of the RM12 stator were $5\frac{7}{16}$ in. across the hexagon and $5\frac{7}{8}$ in. spigot diameter with a width of $1\frac{1}{2}$ in. The rotor had flat sides and was $3\frac{1}{4}$ in. diameter and 2 in. wide.

By 1954 there were two new alternators, with the RM14 in the same form as the RM12, except that the stator could be had in thin, intermediate or thick widths. The RM13 was intended for machines with lower gearing and

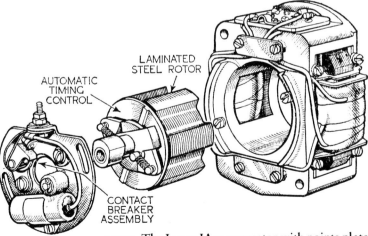

AUTOMATIC TIMING CONTROL

LAMINATED STEEL ROTOR

CONTACT BREAKER ASSEMBLY

ABOVE The Lucas IA45 generator with points plate and advance mechanism

LEFT Checking the gap between rotor and stator

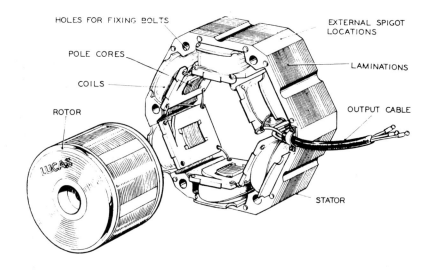

HOLES FOR FIXING BOLTS

POLE CORES

COILS

ROTOR

EXTERNAL SPIGOT
LOCATIONS

LAMINATIONS

OUTPUT CABLE

STATOR

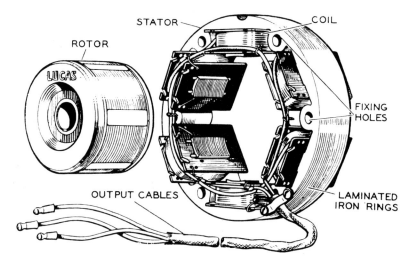

STATOR

COIL

ROTOR

FIXING
HOLES

OUTPUT CABLES

LAMINATED
IRON RINGS

Lucas alternators with the
RM14 above and circular
RM15 below. Either can
have loose coils, so they
should be checked

higher engine speeds and was circular with a 5 in. stator diameter. Its rotor had a recessed side and was smaller at $2\frac{3}{4}$ in. diameter. By 1956 it had been joined by the RM13/15 which had a wider rotor to enable more power to be produced at low speed. It was intended for use in situations where the machine would not run at speed, such as off-road or some police escort duties.

A year later it was joined by the RM15, which was again of 5 in. diameter but wider than the RM13. Lucas also offered the 5AF which was a version of the RM13/15 with a flywheel and cooling fins cast in with the rotor and intended for scooter use. Gearing was added to enable electric starting to be provided.

For 1962 there was a new series of alternators in the form of the RM18, RM19, RM20/19 and scooter-type 9AF. The RM types were progressively wider and the number of rotor laminations were 25, 32 and 45 respect-

ively, while the stator laminations were 14, 16 and 26. The rotors were about 2.9 in. diameter, straight-sided and able to accommodate a drive shaft up to 1 in. diameter.

Finally came the RM21, which had the stator windings encapsulated so they were less prone to damage but were nearly impossible to repair if there was an internal fault. It was followed by the high-output RM23 and the three-phase RM24.

The rectifier

This must be kept clean and dry, in a cool location, and its connections must be in good order. Usually one of these is the centre bolt which therefore must either earth to the frame or have a lead connected to it.

Many rectifiers comprise a series of plates clamped together by their centre bolt and their correct operation is determined by this pres-

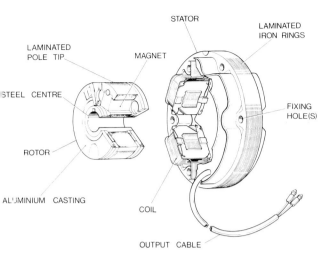

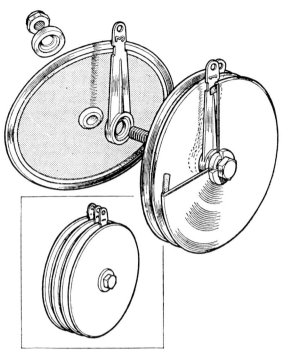

ABOVE The later encapsulated RM Lucas alternator

RIGHT Early STC Sentercel rectifier showing build up. In practice, the centre nut must never be moved

sure. Under no circumstances should the clamp nut be disturbed, a point which must be watched when removing or fitting the rectifier. If the plates themselves are twisted, the electrical connection will be broken with the same effect of ruining the component.

The full-wave rectifier has four connections with one of these usually going to the machine earth. Thus, this must match the battery polarity and the correct rectifier be fitted. The second direct-current connection will go to the battery live terminal, often via the ammeter and switch.

The two alternating-current terminals are joined to the alternator and can be reversed, as this will not affect the operation of the system. They lie either side of the direct-current terminal and so can be readily identified if not marked.

The rectifier can be tested electrically, either on or off the machine, using a meter and a resistive load, but on the machine this must be done at the correct speeds and conditions. For most owners a simple check with a meter or battery and bulb will indicate whether the four elements are in good order, allowing current to flow in one direction and not the other.

Lucas system wiring

On a six-volt system with switch control and

emergency start, this can be quite complex. Many variations exist to cater for machine needs and the one chosen can depend on whether coil or magneto ignition is fitted, or whether the engine runs at low speed with a heavy electrical load. There is also energy transfer, booster coils and stop-light feed in some instances. Plus amendments to raise or lower the charge and for special cases.

You are referred to the wiring diagram for

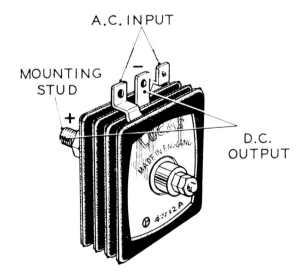

Later selenium metal plate rectifier with less volume and more capacity

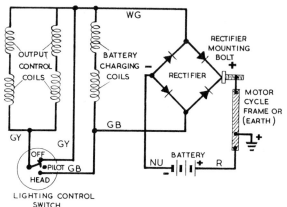

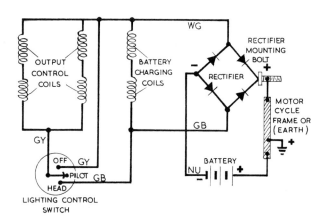

your machine to determine exactly what you should have.

The most usual arrangement is for machines with coil or magneto ignition, and takes the six coils as three pairs. Each pair of coils is in series and thus joined end to end. The three pairs have one wire end joined as a common lead out, while the other ends have one by itself and the other two joined.

Thus, the three output wires are joined to one, two or three coil pairs, and it is one and three that go to the alternating terminals at the rectifier. The wire colours changed twice because the originals faded and became hard to tell apart. The wires connected to the one, two and three coil pairs were at first dark green, mid-green and light green, respectively. They then changed to dark green, green and yellow, and light green. Their final colours were green and black, green and yellow, and green and white.

It was the connection of the two-coil wire that was used to change the output, and in the lowest output condition it was joined to the three-coil wire. When a magneto was fitted, this joint was broken when the parking light came on, which increased the output as the two coil pairs no longer produced an opposing magnetic field against that of the pair in the circuit and generating.

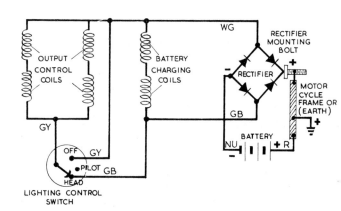

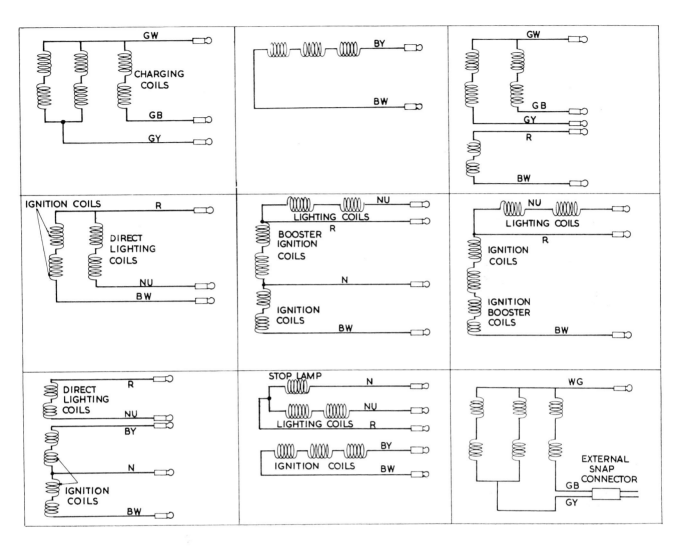

For a machine with coil ignition, this joint would stay as it was when the parking lights went on. Conversely, the wiring could be such that in either case the joint was not made. The final condition occurred when the headlight was switched on and this joined the one- and two-coil wires so all three pairs were wired in parallel and the output was a maximum.

From this base there are variations, the simplest being a boost switch to join the one- and two-coil wires to give full output regardless of the light-switch position. The emergency-start arrangements take the output from four coils to the ignition coil by using the two-coil wire already connected to the light switch. In this condition the engine may misfire but can soon be returned to normal ignition.

The emergency ignition should not be used for longer than is necessary and its effectiveness will depend on the timing. This is because it is a form of energy-transfer ignition and thus

dependent on the peaks of the alternating-current waveform.

There are two further charge rates that can be used by switching the wire connections from the alternator and joining the one-coil wire to the two-coil wire in the harness, and vice versa. The effect is that four coils, in two pairs, are permanently connected to the rectifier and only one pair is either dormant or joined to the three-coil wire to oppose the field.

Even more wiring complication comes on machines fitted with both dynamo and alternator, as was done for some police, AA and RAC models. There were also special units for use in the USA with its long stretches of straight roads. Low-output stators for this use were part numbers 47171 and 47183, being used up to 1963.

Most of the other winding connections kept the six coils, but not all. One had three coils in series and thus only two output wires which connected to a pair of ignition coils to provide energy-transfer ignition for a twin. Another had four coils as two pairs with one lead common to both pairs and two more for the other two coil ends.

There are various combinations used for energy-transfer ignition plus lights, with three or four coils for the ignition and a pair for the main lights, plus one for a stop light. Some of the coils were there to boost the ignition side and in other cases each pair looked after one cylinder of a twin. Finally, there was the type where an external connector joined the one wire and coil wires to produce the full output situation for a 12-volt system.

It is because of all this complication that you have to use the wiring diagram for your machine, as it is not practical to include all the possibilities in this book. It also makes a very good case for adopting the change set out in the next section!

12 volts and the zener diode

All this complication was swept away when the system voltage was changed to 12 volts and control was by a zener diode. This simply connected between the supply-side direct-current terminal of the rectifier and earth.

As the battery voltage rose past 14 volts, the zener began to conduct current from the alternator to earth, and by 15 volts it was sending most of it that way. This bypassed all the control, battery and load-sensing problems in one fell swoop. At first, the zener could not cope with the full alternator output so the six coils were only connected when the headlamp was on. When off, only two coils were in circuit when the machine had magneto ignition and four if it had coil ignition.

This need to continue with switch control soon went as zener diodes improved and were able to deal with the power they had to absorb. This was dissipated by some form of heat sink which should be a flat alloy plate or a finned carrier. Norton Commandos chose to differ from the rest by using one or both of the alloy footrest supports for the job.

It is easy and beneficial to convert a machine to 12 volts. Most of the work involves changing components to those suited to the higher voltage and reducing the wiring to a much simpler form. The procedure depends on the machine and the main points to remember are

A zener diode mounted on its finned heat sink which looked so much better than a flat metal plate

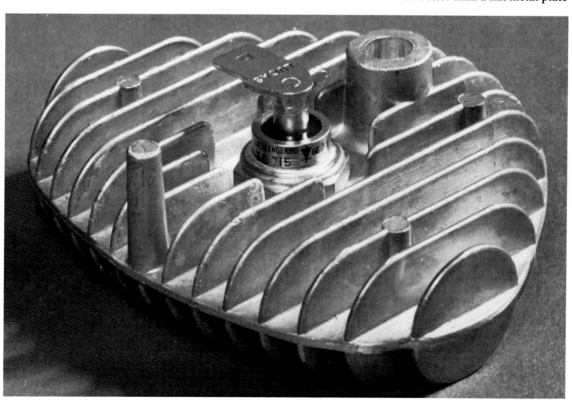

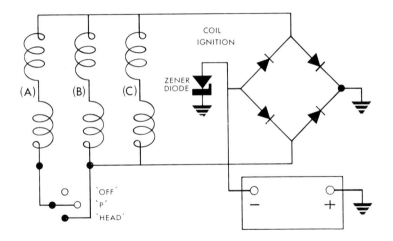

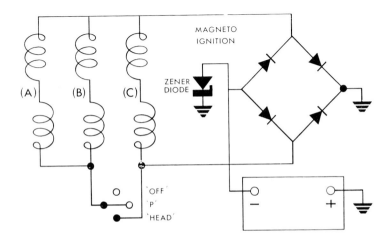

The 12-volt zener-diode control circuit in two forms to suit coil or magneto ignition

to provide a good size of heat sink for the zener diode to be fixed to, use rectifier Lucas part 49072, fit a 12-volt coil and capacitor, change the bulbs, and either add a second 6-volt battery or fit a 12-volt one. The horn can be changed or left as it is.

The RM23 alternator requires two zener diodes to control it on the Norton and late Triumph applications, and these need to be a matched pair connected by the right length and type of wire. The three-phase RM24 requires a six-diode rectifier to deal with its three output leads.

These late-type systems work well but can still suffer troubles. If one leg of the rectifier goes, the battery will run down. One symptom may be that the headlight dims when the stop light goes on. Should the zener short, the fuse will blow—but if it goes open circuit, there will be no voltage control and a boiled battery is the result. Riding with the lights on will help on the ride home or to a supply shop. The same thing works where the zener has shorted and has been disconnected.

BTH alternator

This was developed during World War 2 and was much as the early Lucas alternator, except that it was a 12-pole device with 12 coils wound on the stator. Its output was 36 watts and the headlight switch was used to connect the supply lead to a resistor when the light was off.

A metal rectifier enabled the battery for the horn and parking and tail lights to be charged, and this supply was via a thermostatic cut-out which isolated the battery when the generator was not charging.

The original 6 in. diameter alternator was later joined by a larger $7\frac{1}{4}$ in. one, and this gave out 50 watts. It was used on the Triumph TRW side-valve twin ridden by the armed services.

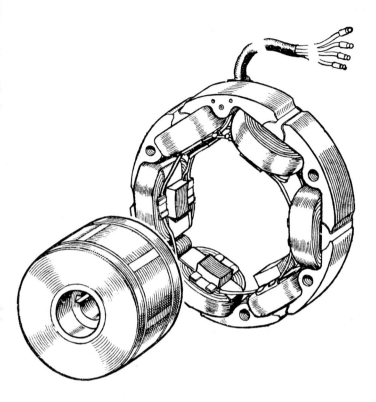

A Wipac Series 114 alternator which was much as the Lucas design with six coils

Miller alternator

Though this company was better known for its dynamo and flywheel magnetos, it also made a 60-watt alternator. It was of the six-pole type with the rotor being either a taper or a splined fit to the engine mainshaft.

Switch control of the output was used, along with an emergency start using the full alternator output. Its main use was on the LE Velocette where it replaced the original BTH dynamo, but a version also went on the Royal Enfield Clipper and Douglas Dragonfly flat twin of 1955, and NSU-Vincent machines of that period.

Wico-Pacy alternator

This was a six-pole type, much as the Lucas, and was originally listed for the Triumph Terrier, although few, if any, of these were so equipped. Switch charge control was used.

Later versions were used by AMC for their 250 cc models, the Ariel Colt, C10L BSA, various scooters, Excelsior, Francis-Barnett, James, and Norton 250 and 350 twins, along with various other applications.

Regulation was in part by a resistance wire included in the harness or by a relay-type regulator box in addition to the usual full-wave rectifier. The same set of requirements as to cleaning, inspection and good connections apply, just as for any other make of equipment.

CHAPTER 10
Starters

Most machines that are restored just have a kickstarter which falls into the transmission area. Nowadays, many have electric starters, all of which work on the same principle as an electric motor.

The motor looks very much the same as a dynamo with an armature, having a commutator, brushes and a field winding. The difference is that the field is in series with the armature and some heavy currents are involved in order to get the power needed to turn the engine on a cold morning.

Due to these heavy currents, all wires are kept short and thick, including those of the field winding. Often there are four brushes simply to spread the load which two would not be able to stand up to without burning.

This is the drive-motor side of the starter, but it also has another aspect, namely the mechanical drive from the motor to the engine.

The Lucas M3 starter motor with pre-engaged drive and main power switch on its back

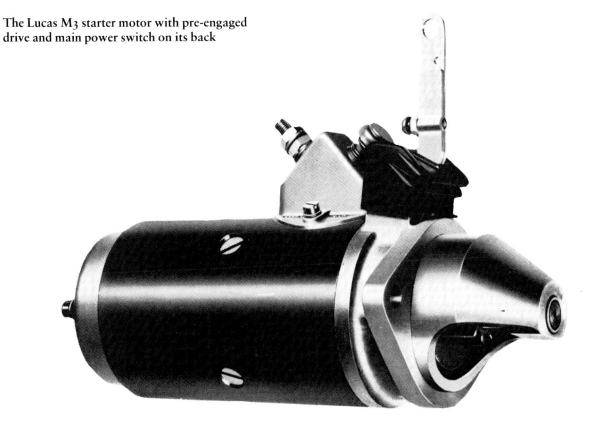

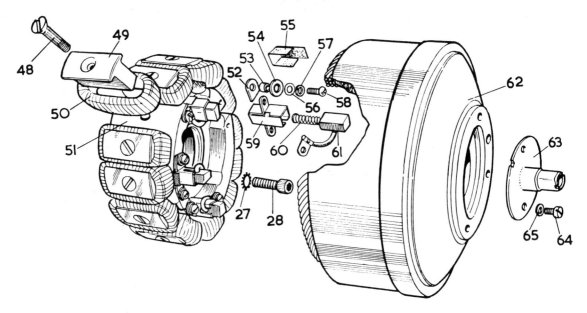

On the Dynastart, and other similar combined dynamo and starter assemblies, the unit is mounted on the end of the crankshaft and so drives directly. However, this form is only able to cope with small two-stroke engines, though it works well with them as long as the switch-gear is in order.

All other starters have some form of mechanical drive which may be an inertia engagement, pre-engaged or one-way clutch drive. A reduction gear is usually included in the arrangement one way or another.

Starter service

Most of this is much as for a dynamo, with the cleaning of parts, checking of brushes for length and free movement, inspection of commutator, and metering of field coil for continuity and insulation.

Due to the currents involved, *all* connections must be clean and tight. It only takes one to be a little slack for the starter not to work at all. This is the most common reason for failure but is easy to guard against.

The starter can be dismantled much as the dynamo and its armature checked electrically for insulation and open or shorted coils. The commutator can be cleaned or skimmed and the mica insulation between its segments undercut as for the dynamo. The brushes may need replacement if well worn and must be free to move in their housings.

The starter drive needs cleaning and examination. Various types exist but can be divided into those brought into mesh when needed and

ABOVE Siba Dynastart combined dynamo and starter with its face commutator

BELOW Drive system as used by the Triumph Bonneville in 1980, with connections to the timing gears

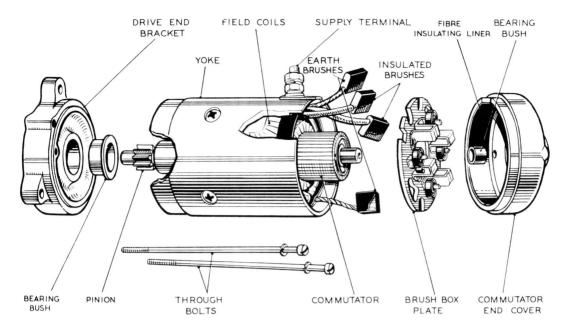

DRIVE END BRACKET

FIELD COILS

SUPPLY TERMINAL

FIBRE INSULATING LINER

BEARING BUSH

YOKE

EARTH BRUSHES

INSULATED BRUSHES

BEARING BUSH

PINION

THROUGH BOLTS

COMMUTATOR

BRUSH BOX PLATE

COMMUTATOR END COVER

ABOVE The Lucas M3 starter motor in exploded form to show its construction

BELOW Starter-motor epicyclic reduction gears (top) and sprag crankshaft clutch (bottom), which were united by chain

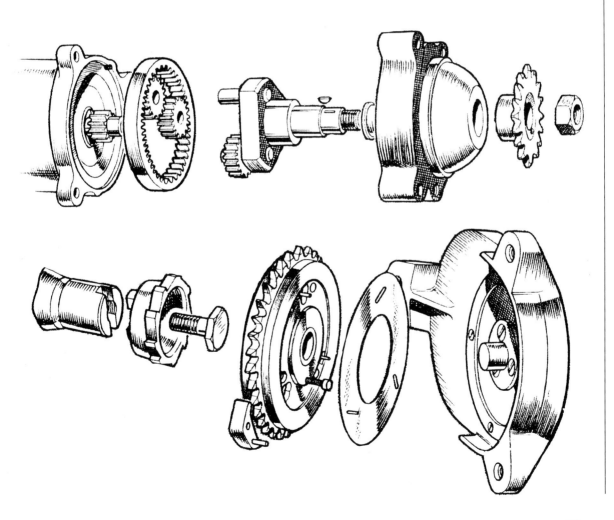

those permanently engaged with an override clutch. The first may be pre-engaged with a manual lever or a solenoid that also closes the main supply contacts once in mesh. An alternative is the inertia, or Bendix, drive, where the gear is flung into engagement by the start-up of the motor. These seldom give trouble, but if they do, a good clean will often rectify this or enable the cause to be detected.

The other type has some form of sprag clutch in the drive that allows the engine to run faster than the starter, which can freewheel or not turn at all. Most comprise a number of rollers with springs behind them to force them up a ramp and into engagement with a drum so that the drive only occurs in one direction. The springs and rollers may need changing if worn and the drum should be inspected as it may wear generally or in ridges.

The combined dynamo and starter, such as the Siba Dynastart equipment, has been mentioned in the dynamo section, and six of its 12 coils were used for starting. There were two pairs of brushes to deal with each function and servicing of the unit was as already described.

Starter relay and button

Owing to the heavy currents involved, a relay is used to connect the starter to the battery. This is a simple electro-magnetic type and its coil is energized when the starter button is pressed.

Both relay and button should be clean with all connections, especially the heavy-gauge ones, good and tight. The units can be checked electrically with a meter and if there is still a problem, even when they are in order, check for other switches in the button line. Some machines have the wiring arranged so that the starter will not work if the machine is in gear but will if the clutch is pulled in. Others insist on the machine being in neutral. Also check that the seldom-used kill switch is not involved and causing a problem because its contacts have corroded.

The Lucas M3 starter motor in direct-drive form, with the solenoid used to operate it

CHAPTER 11
Battery and wiring

The battery is the heart of the electrical system, and the wiring and connections are the most common reasons for trouble and faults. A battery in good condition gives the system a stable base to work from—without it, both the charging and using sides of the circuit will be in trouble.

The wiring joins all the parts of the system together. It includes the earth return, whether that is via the frame or by wire, and each wire is as important as the components and details of the major system units. Their two troubles are either losing the connection, one way or another, or making a wrong connection, either to earth or to another wire.

All the trauma this can cause can be avoided with care and by making sure that the wires, connections and switches are all doing their job. All are important, as the electricity will not mind where there is a weak spot—it will just choose the easiest route for itself, as always.

Battery

This may be 6 or 12 volts and must be large enough to provide the reserve the machine needs. Where an electric starter is fitted, the battery ought to be able to turn the cold engine over in the depths of winter, but not all can manage this.

As the temperature drops, so too does the battery output. Thus, in deep winter an electric start can call for a massive battery. Few older machines provide this, relying instead on the owner kickstarting the engine when the weather is at its worst.

Without a starter, the battery merely has to act as a reservoir for the ignition and parking lights and can therefore be much smaller. Fitting a larger battery only enlarges the reservoir and by itself will not improve the lights or anything else. It will allow supplementary lights to be used for longer, even if they overload the system, and some owners fit them for that reason.

Most machines have a single battery of the appropriate voltage, but some with a 12-volt system fit two of 6 volts. This is quite in order and may be done when converting to 12 volts. The two batteries do not need to be mounted side by side or even be the same size, although they should not be too different. The one point that matters is that the join between them is

Typical 12-volt battery with its six cells

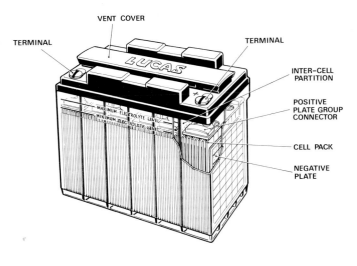

from the positive of one to the negative of the other.

As the battery does not like vibration, it should be rubber mounted in some way. It needs to be securely held in place but the clamp must not strain the case; most use a rubber strap in some form or other. This must be in good condition and not likely to snap at the wrong moment. If it also prevents the cell filler plugs from working loose and becoming lost, this will be a further bonus and is a small, but worthwhile, alteration that can be made in some cases. The battery case and terminals should be kept clean and the electrolyte topped up. Only use distilled water for this job as the battery may not like the chemicals in tap water. Petroleum jelly on the terminals will help to keep corrosion at bay, especially if the battery fumes due to overcharging.

Specific gravity

The battery comprises a series of cells, each developing two volts, so there are three for a 6-volt and six for a 12-volt battery. Each cell has a series of lead plates in a dilute sulphuric-acid solution, and the charge and discharge process as current flows in and out comes from or causes chemical reactions.

These reactions are reversible without gain or loss, but if there is too much charging some of the water in the electrolyte is lost, so this becomes stronger. Topping up restores this, only requiring water as none of the acid is lost.

The state of charge also affects the cell voltage and the specific gravity of the electrolyte. Neat sulphuric acid weighs 1.84 times the same amount of water, thus having a specific gravity (or sg) of 1.84. When diluted for a fully-charged battery, it reduces to 1.28, and when discharged it falls to 1.13 because there is more water in the mixture.

By measuring the sg with a hydrometer, the state of charge can be checked. Only use a small instrument on a motorcycle battery or you will not get enough liquid for a true measurement. Do not take a reading just after topping up, as this will be false, but let the battery work a little first. All cells should be similar and a marked disparity could indicate a dead cell and the need for a replacement battery.

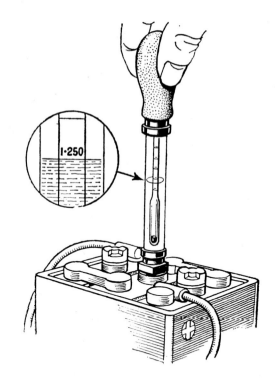

Checking the specific gravity with a small hydrometer, and the desired reading shown inset

Battery polarity and connection

The current always flows round the circuit from positive to negative, but either terminal can be the one taken to earth. The battery must always be connected correctly for the machine it goes with or problems will arise, especially with any equipment involving electronics.

For many years the convention was to earth the negative terminal and this applies to most machines up to about 1951–52. At this point a change to positive earth began to be made, although not all models altered to this immediately. This situation remained for many years, but in recent times there has been a move back to negative earth.

If in doubt, check and double-check.

When disconnecting the battery it is always best to remove the earthed wire first, regardless as to which earth system the machine has. This is so that if the spanner or screwdriver you use touches the machine frame, it will not matter — nor will it short out the battery, which can be quite exciting with lots of sparks. With the earth lead off, the supply one can then be removed. If the tool touches the frame then, it will not complete a circuit so there won't be trouble. Reverse the procedure when connecting the battery back into place.

Restoration and the battery

The battery can give the restorer a number of problems, beginning with its storage if in good order. It should not be left to itself as that will be its downfall. If it has a charge, it should be left connected to a 3-watt bulb until it is discharged, and then charged up again.

This action needs to be repeated periodically every two or three weeks, with the battery always left in a fully-charged state. This is because in this condition it will not freeze until about −60 degrees Celsius, but if discharged it will freeze around −10 degrees Celsius and could then split its case. In addition, if left discharged, sulphation of the plates will occur which will ruin the battery if left for too long.

A problem of appearance occurs when the battery is externally mounted and not in a box or under the seat behind a side cover. It is possible to obtain a replica of the old-style black battery which is one solution. Another is to use an old case from which the interior has been removed and fit a modern battery in this.

When doing this, or, in fact, when carrying out any work on the battery, care and caution should be exercised due to the dangers of handling acid. Points to watch for are never to use a match or naked flame near the battery vents as the vapour they may give off can be combustible. If the battery has spilt any electrolyte you will need to add acid and this must be done with great care. Always add the acid to the water or electrolyte, or the heat generated could make the liquid erupt and be thrown about. If in any doubt, ask a chemist to do this.

The dry battery

Normally this refers to a primary cell, such as the type used in a torch which is discarded when run down. However, there was the Varley Dry Accumulator which acted as a normal battery but held the electrolyte in suspension. Thus, the cell could be inverted and was often used by owners who rode in a trial at the weekend. Their headlight might be easy to detach but many would leave the battery, and full charging system, in place for the event. As the Varley prevented spillage and damaged paint, it was very popular in this field.

Its care and maintenance are as for any other battery, but the type is no longer available, although the firm is still in the battery business.

Some two-stroke lightweights with direct lighting need a dry battery for parking lights often located in the headlamp shell. If left and neglected, this can leak and corrode the surrounding metal.

SEPARATORS

NEGATIVE
OXIDE

POSITIVE
OXIDE

ABOVE **The Varley Dry Accumulator, which acted as a secondary cell but had no free liquid so it could be inverted**

RIGHT **True dry battery used to power the parking light of this small Villiers headlamp**

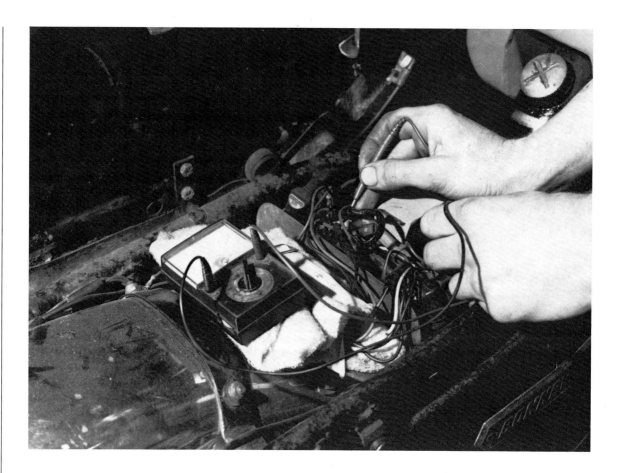

Wiring

This joins all the parts of the system together and each wire needs to be of the correct size for its job, properly insulated, well connected and not damaged in any way.

The wiring is usually bound into a harness and is thus an assembly which needs to be carefully checked for damage or chafing. The section that runs past the headstock is always suspect, due to the bending that occurs when the forks turn and the grease that may leak from the head races. The ends of the harness that run to the tail light also seem prone to more damage than the rest of the harness.

The harness should be laid out and checked with a meter. It is necessary to know where each end connects to, and you will need the wiring diagram or layout for this. The individual wires are identified either with numbered or coloured sleeves on their ends or by colour coding of the insulation. When carrying out the check you need to look for a connection from end to end of each wire, even when the harness is moved or bent as it would be on the machine. You also need to be sure that no wire

Checking the electrics with a meter and probe, a tool which makes fault finding so much easier

is connected to another that it should in fact be insulated from.

Early wiring had rubber insulation which may crack or perish, so although a harness of this type may be no trouble when the weather is fine, it can give many problems in the damp or wet. Modern wiring has a plastic insulation and trouble in the harness itself is rare—nearly all the problems arise at the connections or due to obvious damage. This last usually occurs either because the wires have been allowed to chafe on sharp edges and through not being clamped, or because the harness has been trapped and crushed or cut at some point. Beneath the petrol tank is the favourite one, but there are others.

Wire size and colour code

Each wire is made up of a number of fine strands of copper wire wound into a length and then insulated. The wire tries to resist the flow of electricity and the effect it will have depends on the amount trying to flow (that is, the current), the pressure or voltage behind it, and the wire characteristics. These amount to its length, cross-sectional area, material and temperature.

The last two are effectively fixed, but the length and area can vary considerably. If the area is small and the current high, there will be a good deal of resistance which will raise the temperature of the wire. This will be made worse if the wire is lengthy.

Thus, wires carrying heavy currents need to be short and fat. An extreme example of this is the starter wiring which is always very heavy, but the same thing affects all wires which must be fully ample for what they have to carry. The earth return must not be forgotten in this respect as it is very much part of the circuit and may have to carry the current back from several items.

Wire sizes are given as the number of strands and the strand diameter, and may be in imperial or metric dimensions. In the first you may find 23/0.0076 and in the second 14/0.30, which translates to 23 strands of wire of 0.0076 in. diameter and 14 strands of 0.30 mm wire. Some metric circuits also specify the area of each wire in mm², and the number is likely to be 0.75, 1, 2.5 or 16 for the starter. More strands are usually better than fewer for two reasons: the first is that the wire will be more flexible and less likely to fracture due to vibration, and the second that when a wire or two are nicked, while removing the insulation for a connector, it will have less effect on the area. An extreme example in flexibility is the wire used to earth the contact plates in some Lucas car distributors. It has a very large number of strands of hair-like wire and behaves like a piece of wet string as it responds to the movements of the plate over many years of use.

Always err on the larger size for area as this will reduce the voltage drop in the wire, which is especially important on a 6-volt system. Thus use 23/0.0076 rather than 14/0.0076.

Colour codes have some degree of standardization in that most machines with Lucas electrics will have similar coding. This can always be varied, so be prepared for changes that either the maker or past owners may have incorporated.

A final cable to consider is the high-tension one which is usually 7 mm diameter and heavily insulated. This is due to the high voltage it has to pass, but the actual wire can be quite thin as the current involved is small.

Earth

The major cause of electrical troubles is the earth, as most older machines rely on the current wending its way back to the battery via many junctions between the frame parts—a common earth point, often near the seat nose, then connects battery and frame, and in a few cases may also connect to the headlamp shell. If it does not, the control cables and head races have to help out.

The earth connection is as much a part of the circuit as anything else and must be treated as such. The best answer is either to bypass the frame altogether and use an earth return wire for all items, or to use this to supplement the frame. This method will also overcome any problems with parts that are rubber mounted. In either case, an earth connection should be made to both frame and engine unit. The last is involved in both the ignition and generator circuits.

Do not forget the earth connection to the rectifier and zener diode and make sure that all wires are adequate for the job and are making good contact.

Switches

These come in many shapes and forms, so in this context they can include buttons which are simply spring-loaded switches. All need to be checked for operation and most need notes taken as to which terminals are joined in each switch position.

There are various ways of representing this data, but the best seems to be a small box table showing terminals and wire colours across the tops of the columns, with the switch positions on the left under each other. Horizontal lines can then clearly show which terminals are joined for each position. Most of the circular presentations make too much of an attempt to look like the switch itself and thus fail to show the connections. This picture should be used to supplement the first but only to establish terminal positions.

The main switch used for Lucas systems with Mag-dyno is fairly simple and can be dismantled for cleaning. Do note that the contact

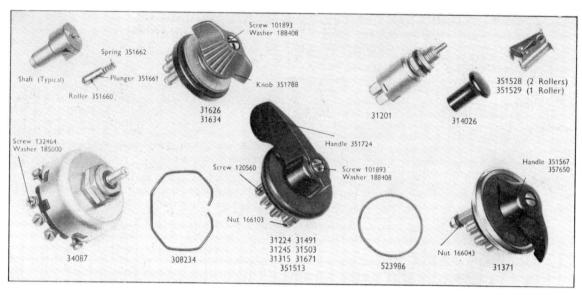

Screw 101893
Washer 188408

Spring 351662

Shaft (Typical)

Plunger 351661

Roller 351660

Knob 351788

31626
31634

Screw 132464
Washer 185000

31201

314026

351528 (2 Rollers)
351529 (1 Roller)

Handle 351724

Screw 120560

Screw 101893
Washer 188408

Handle 351567
357650

Nut 166103

Nut 166043

34087

308234

31224 31491
31245 31503
31315 31671
351513

523986

31371

LIGHTING DIMMER SWITCH ARRANGEMENT — IGNITION STARTER SWITCH SWITCH

	IG	HB	TL	LB		KB	KW		ST	E
H	O─O─O					OFF			OFF	
ON N	O─O─O─O					ON	O─O			
L	O───O─O					OFF			ON	O─O
OFF										

ABOVE Some of the Lucas switches as shown in their catalogue, together with spares

LEFT Switch-connection diagram which all owners should work out for their machine, as without it you will be lost

roller in the centre spindle has a carrier and spring behind it, all of which will try to escape to the floor given half a chance. The same switch for coil ignition is more complex due to the ignition key and terminals in the centre.

Most switches with contact rollers can be dismantled, including dip switches, but beware of those with small detail parts. They can be easily lost and some are awkward to assemble without some form of jig or tool to hold parts in place. If you are stuck, it is normally possible to get the more complex or difficult switch together again, but there are also those you will wish you had never started on.

While some switches use rollers to make contacts, others use spring-loaded rings or blades. Some of these types are held together with a clip or several bent lugs on one part which lock to another. These can normally be prised back to release them, but expect the assembly to fly apart, and be ready to work out how it all goes back together.

It is therefore necessary to check terminals and switch positions so you can be sure you have it all back where it came from. Another, and similar, type of switch has leaf-spring contacts and may be easier to cope with as it will be less likely to fly apart.

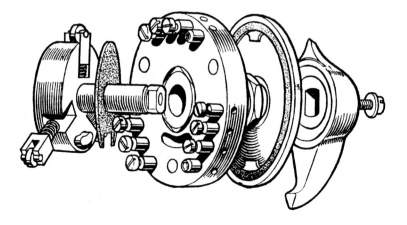

A Wipac switch with rollers and springs to make the contacts

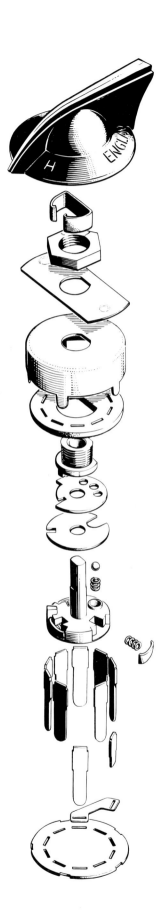

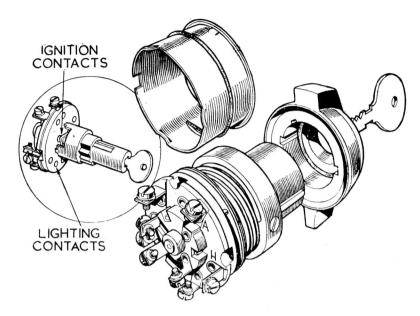

IGNITION
CONTACTS

LIGHTING
CONTACTS

ABOVE Lucas lighting switch combined with central ignition switch, as used by early BSA Bantams

LEFT Component parts of a switch which plugs into a socket wired into the harness

BELOW Combined lights and ignition switch for the BSA 250s and Sunbeams of the early 1950s

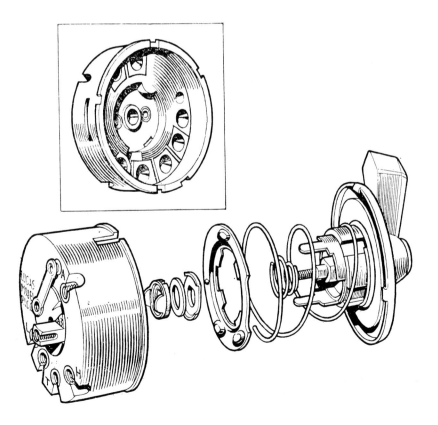

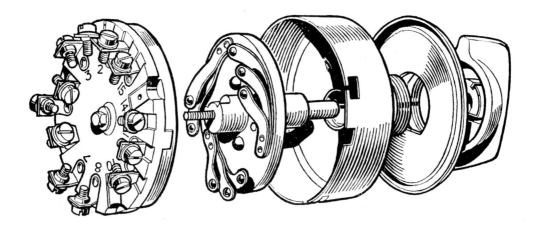

ABOVE Later Lucas switch with leaf contact springs

RIGHT Britax twistgrip dip switch, sold as an extra for the left handlebar

BELOW Wipac dip switch with make-before-break contacts, essential with direct lighting

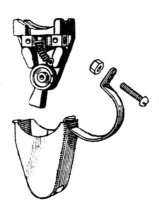

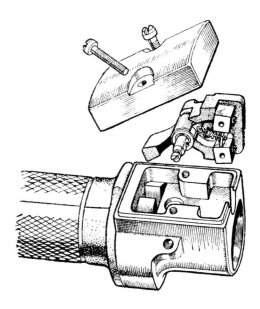

Some switches are very simple, among these being the horn or cut-out button, basic dip switch and on/off switches. The brake stop-light switch is one such adapted to suit its purpose and often fails due to the weather conditions it has to work under.

More complex switches control the lights and sometimes also the alternator output which, if incorporated with ignition in normal and emergency states, can have a good number of terminals, as many as 18 in some cases. This is usual where there are two separate switches built into the one assembly. Other types have more functions and are usually handlebar mounted.

From the simple horn button came a combined part with horn and cut-out buttons plus dip switch. More modern machines have more extensive control of the lights, horn, headlamp flasher and turn indicator, all in a single assembly.

One of the less common switches is that used by the early BSA Bantam, with handlebar control connected by cable to a switch mounted within the headlamp shell. It gave four positions of 'Off', 'Full', 'Dip' and 'Park', and both switch and control can be dismantled, cleaned and repaired.

Later came the two-part plug-in switch. This comprised a switch with pin connections in its rear and a mating socket that was permanently wired into the harness. This was a useful move that made removal easy, but it is well worth checking out the connections at their wire ends

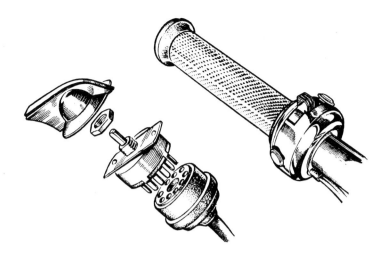

LEFT **Plug-in switch and harness on left and combined dip, horn and cut-out controls on right, both from Wipac**

BELOW **Early BSA Bantam had its headlamp switch controlled from handlebar lever connected by cable**

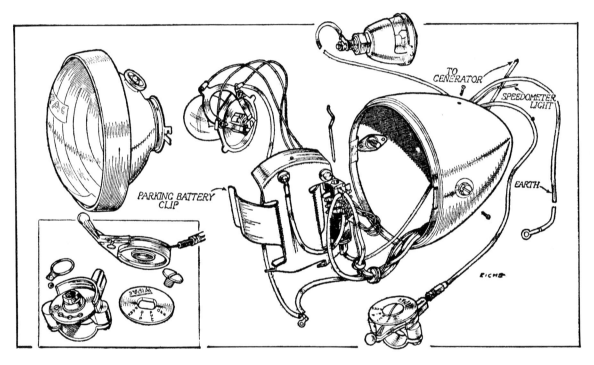

just to make sure. Faults in the switch or the harness were rare, but in making the junction at the plug-in could be frequent. Often the clip that is supposed to hold them together becomes bent and fails to achieve its aim. This is a common cause of problems as the contact can be intermittent, and this can be the hardest to sort out.

Connections

The wires have to be joined to one another and to the electrical components, and at each join there is the very real possibility of trouble with a poor connection. Every single join must be properly made, whether in a supply or return line, and any lapse in this can cause all manner

of problems. In the main, the connections should be kept to a minimum, as every extra one can spell trouble, but some owners like to be able to separate the tail section from the main harness.

Some joints may involve soldering, for which a good clean iron is needed, with care taken to avoid a dry joint. A dry joint is one that looks reasonable but in fact makes a very poor electrical or mechanical junction. It is equally important not to let the solder run too far up the wire from the connector, as this makes the wire rigid and more prone to breakage under vibration.

On older machines, the wire end may be held by a grub screw in some form of post at the switch. The post is slotted for the wire and

105

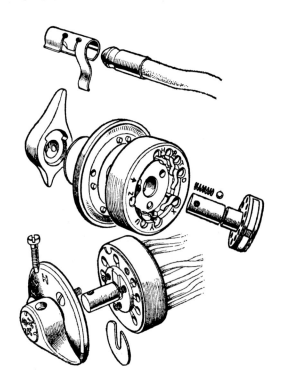

Two-part Lucas switches for ignition and lights which plug into the harness but must make good contact

BTH switch in which the wires plug into sockets acting as the contacts for the rotor

some owners solder the wire end to form a tag for the screw to bear against. The only snag with this is a tendency for the wire to fracture just outboard of the post unless it is well supported and clamped into place. Possibly, a better way is to roll the wire end into a loop or ball which cannot easily pull out from the post. It may require the screw to be removed to fix the wire in place but the increased security is well worth the added effort.

With all switches with this type of connection, it is important to make sure that all the strands have been collected under the correct post screw. It is quite easy for one or two to escape and bridge over to an adjacent post with all kinds of odd effects.

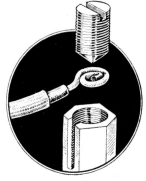

Old-style terminal post and screw with coiled wire end

The other common older form of connection is the ring which is fixed to a stud with a nut and spring washer. This is common for ammeters and is dependent on the ring being clean and well anchored to the wire. This type gives better support to the wire if it has clamps for both the wire and the insulation. Avoid the cheaper type which only holds the wire, as a fracture can easily occur. Solder the wire to the terminal for complete security.

A variation of this type is the open ring which has the advantage that you do not need to remove the nut or screw to make the connection. In its basic form it is less secure than the ring, but it, and the blade it is fixed to, can easily be formed so that it is locked in place until the fixing is backed off two or three turns. The same care is needed in attaching the wire which may be crimped or soldered in place.

Another connection used by Lucas for some lamps is a simple thimble which the bared wire passes through and is then turned back on. The housing receptacle for this is a spring blade wound into a circle into which the thimble is forced so the housing holds on to the wire ends. With this type, be wary of pushing the thimble too far and making a connection with another terminal.

From this type of connection, Lucas went on to the in-line snap connector (or bullet connec-

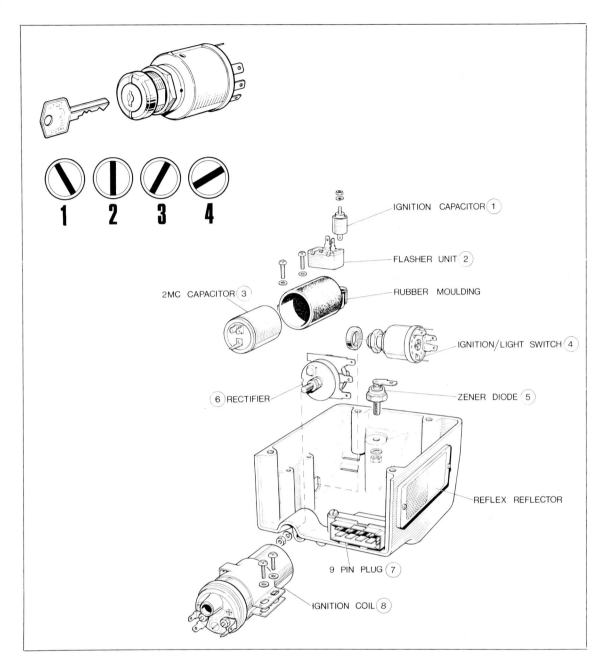

IGNITION CAPACITOR ①

FLASHER UNIT ②

2MC CAPACITOR ③

RUBBER MOULDING

IGNITION/LIGHT SWITCH ④

⑥ RECTIFIER

ZENER DIODE ⑤

REFLEX REFLECTOR

9 PIN PLUG ⑦

IGNITION COIL ⑧

1 2 3 4

tor) with the cable ends swaged and soldered on to the wires. The connector was a rolled section into which the wire ends clicked and the whole was insulated by a rubber sleeve. From the basic single join came multiples allowing three, four or five wires to be joined while remaining apart from each other. Where a compound join was needed, a double connector was used which enabled four wires to join together.

This connector can be prone to corrosion, and making or breaking the joints can be awkward. It is also possible to pull the wire out

Lucas electrics box which combined most parts in one unit—this is easy to remove for bench work

of the end, but even if this does not happen, it may no longer make the best contact. If in any doubt, peel off the sleeve and check the parts.

The next move was to the push-on, spring-blade connector which had a number of advantages. It could be mass-produced and was easy to fit to the wire using automatic equipment. It was also easy to add on an insulating cover for the connection, while the terminal blade could easily be incorporated in the part to which it would be connected. The contact was easy to connect or part without tools, although a small pair of pliers can be helpful if it is stiff.

This type can also be used to replace others and in this form usually has the cable held by crimped tags with the wire soldered. As always, a good joint will remove a trouble-spot. This type relies on its spring pressure to make a good connection so this must be adequate. If it is stiff to move, it should be fine.

There are other ways to join wires and all kinds of crimp connectors are available for this job. They simply clamp into the wire without any need to strip the insulation and are very handy for making repairs or for taking an extra lead from an existing one.

Again, it must be emphasized that any crimped connection must be secure, as it is only too easy for it to be slightly loose and not make contact as it should.

Harness-making

This is best done on the machine to make sure it all fits. It can be built up in this way and then removed as a unit and bound.

Tape or heat-shrink tubing can be used to bind and protect the wires, but make sure that the assembly is not pulled short by the binding and that it is free enough to move around the headstock with the forks. In all other areas it must be securely held to prevent chafing or wire fracture.

Fuses

These are seldom found on older machines but are well worth adding as an insurance. A single 35-amp fuse in the main battery line can save the day if you suffer a short circuit. If you wish for more sophistication, more fuses can be added.

The easiest way to do this is to use a modern fuse box, with several fuses plus spares. This can be wired into the circuits to protect the various functions. If you have a fuse, watch for corrosion of the ends and the mounting clips, and should a fuse seem to make intermittent contact, change it in case it is at fault.

Carry spares, and if one blows, check for why before replacing it. Do not fit a higher-rated fuse, or a nail, in the hope that this will cure the trouble. It won't—it will simply amplify it!

CHAPTER 12
Lighting and
the law

Electric lighting for motorcycles was available back in Edwardian days, but it did not become a normal fitment until the 1930s. Prior to that time, many riders either went without, using their machines mainly in the summer, or fitted acetylene lighting.

Effectively, this consisted of gas lamps with a chemical generator and remained popular for many years, despite its various minor operating snags and the major need to clean it out fully every time it was used. Without doing this, corrosion and blockages would soon occur, but the system was simple, self-contained, cheap and gave a good light.

In contrast, an electric system either relied on the battery alone or required a dynamo to be added to the machine with drive and cutout. The first meant recharging the battery at home, at a time when many houses relied on gas for their lights, as well as cooking, and were without electricity. Batteries were neither cheap nor long-lasting, so this was a further obstacle.

Adding a dynamo meant also adding a battery and some form of regulation which might have to rely on the rider turning a switch. It added up to an expensive solution even when Lucas produced the Mag-dyno, which at least removed the problem of fixing up a drive.

There were other devices, such as the BTH Sparklight, but few worked well. Even by the late 1920s, many machines were still without

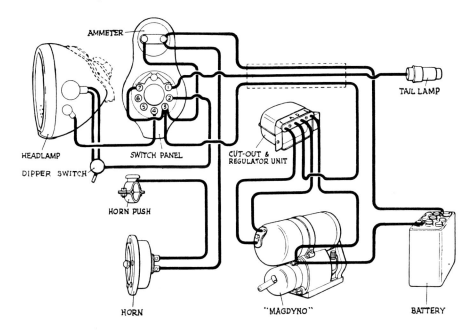

The basic Lucas
Mag-dyno
wiring diagram
as used for many
years

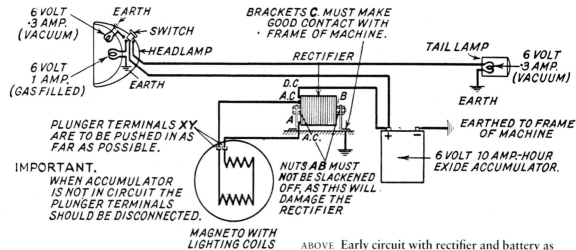

6 VOLT
·3 AMP.
(VACUUM)

EARTH

SWITCH

HEADLAMP

6 VOLT
1 AMP.
(GAS FILLED)

EARTH

BRACKETS **C.** MUST MAKE
GOOD CONTACT WITH
· FRAME OF MACHINE.

RECTIFIER

TAIL LAMP

6 VOLT
·3 AMP.
(VACUUM)

EARTH

EARTHED TO FRAME
OF MACHINE

6 VOLT 10 AMP-HOUR
EXIDE ACCUMULATOR.

D.C
A.C

A.C.

PLUNGER TERMINALS XY
ARE TO BE PUSHED IN AS
FAR AS POSSIBLE.

IMPORTANT.
WHEN ACCUMULATOR
IS NOT IN CIRCUIT THE
PLUNGER TERMINALS
SHOULD BE DISCONNECTED.

NUTS **AB** MUST
NOT BE SLACKENED
OFF, AS THIS WILL
DAMAGE THE
RECTIFIER

MAGNETO WITH
LIGHTING COILS

ABOVE Early circuit with rectifier and battery as used by small two-strokes

LEFT The BTH Sparklight system which used the magneto in an attempt to power the lights

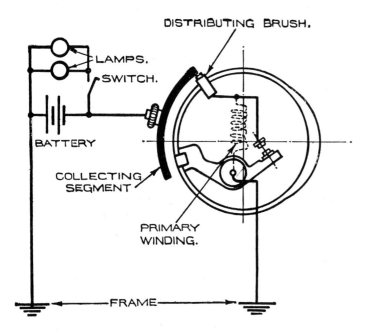

DISTRIBUTING BRUSH.

LAMPS.

SWITCH.

BATTERY

COLLECTING
SEGMENT

PRIMARY
WINDING.

FRAME

As the depression of the 1930s followed, there was great competition to sell machines. This meant that the larger machines had to fall into line with the cheap, economy Villiers jobs and offer full lighting as one of their options. From this struggle for sales came the many options that would be offered for most models and the practice of listing them in basic form at a price that included the lights. For a while, one of the options continued to be acetylene lights, but as the decade progressed this died away as circumstances improved along with the electrics.

So the motorcycle systems came rather late to the field and thus were able to pick up many points from the car world. This included a mass of legislation which has continued to this day.

The law

This section only concerns the United Kingdom and readers are advised to consult local information for other countries. Even for one country the lighting regulations are complex and a trap for the unwary, so the following notes are non-legal and are an attempt to assist rather than to quote legal positions and precedents.

The first point is the need for lights, and in the UK there is no need if the machine is used in daylight hours. It would further appear that

lights or kept to acetylene despite its problems. As more firms offered electric lighting as an option, though, the price began to fall and it became more usual for machines at the top end of the market to have it fitted.

However, it was at the other end of the scale that the breakthrough came when Villiers began to fit lighting coils in their flywheel magneto. These engines were used by many firms who could immediately offer direct lighting without the need for any regulation, and thus at a very favourable price. Before long, a rectifier was also available so that a battery could be added, thus giving the options of direct or battery lighting, or no lighting at all.

a machine without lights can be used in conditions of poor visibility when a machine with lights would be required to have the headlight on. However, although this last may be legal, it is not recommended, as in the event of an accident the police could fall back on their catch-net of 'without due care'. More to the point, your insurance company would repudiate any claim on the basis that riding without lights under poor conditions constituted contributory negligence. At best, they could reduce compensation which could carry serious financial consequences—that is, *you* would pay.

If the conditions really do become too bad to continue, it makes sense to park off-road or at least in a side turning and return for the machine another day. This is a wise course, but make sure it is secure before you leave it. You are allowed to push it along in the left gutter which may enable you to get it to a place of safety under these or other circumstances.

Thus, you can have no lights, which is further defined as meaning none at all and no wiring for lights, so removing the headlamp alone does not qualify. What does qualify is painting or masking the lamp or arranging so that it cannot be used immediately when it is no longer regarded as a lamp.

What it becomes is not stated, but this really is getting into the fine print and not a point to argue about if pulled over. If this happens, simply explain the situation as you see it, note the policeman's number and that of his transport, and if you receive a summons defend the case with legal textbook back-up. I have supplied the data to defence solicitors on this point several times and all have won their case without trouble.

Most owners will have lights and as soon as you join the majority you are subject to all the rules. The first of these is that you must have a full set and they must all work, even the ones that are not always mandatory, such as turn indicators. Fit them and they must comply on size, power, flash rate and all the rest. Unless you run an Electra, it might be easier to forget them.

The lamps you must have in most cases are front, rear and stop, and a means of reading the speedometer and illuminating the rear number plate. For older machines the requirements are fewer, and the bulb power depends on the engine size, machine speed or date first registered.

Dates that crop up are January 1931, 1936, 1972, and April 1986. Sidecars are an odd case but are covered by the rules.

Front lamps are classed as obligatory and headlamp. Of the first, a solo requires one on its centre line or offside, while a sidecar with a headlamp needs one on the centre line of the chair or the side remote from the machine. In practice, this means the normal solo light and one on the chair wheel mudguard.

A headlamp that can be dipped is needed for all except those first used before 1931, those with a 25 mph maximum speed, and under-50 cc machines first used before 1972. All have to fit the lamp on the machine centre line, whether a chair is attached or not. The colour must be white or yellow and the dipped beam can be achieved with the bulb or another lamp. Some pre-war Panther models did this with twin lamps, one of which moved. Now, twin lights should be matched and must work together. If fitted, they are classed as obligatory to cover that requirement.

The headlamp bulb power for machines up

A mid-1950s Miller headlamp with built-in speedometer, ammeter and switches

to 250 cc is 15 watts minimum on both filaments, but those that do not exceed 25 mph only need 10 watts on the dip! For over 250 cc, you need 30-watts main and 24-watts dip as the minimum. After April 1986, a main-beam warning lamp is required.

At the rear you need a red light. No size is now specified, so the early, minute glow-worms are once more legal, although only the foolish would ride ahead of one. While this change in the rules from a specified size helps, the need for a stop light can create problems. The only exemptions are machines that do not exceed 25 mph, those first used before 1936, and those under 50 cc and pre-April 1986. After that April date, all have to be switched on when either the front or the rear brake is used and not, as before, when any brake is used.

Ariel Leader owners are fine with this one until one of their stop-light switches corrodes. The bulb power should be 15–36 watts, or, after April 1986, one with an Approval Mark.

It has been suggested that if the machine has an electrical system that is unable to power a stop light, one does not need to be fitted—but this is not the case.

All machines of any age or size require a rear reflector, and an outfit needs two. All need to be mounted vertically and face squarely to the rear.

Turn signals were not required until April 1986 and are not required on machines not exceeding 25 mph, nor on those built primarily for off-road use and to carry only one person as a solo, or two if a sidecar is fitted and the second person is in that. There are positional and view-angle requirements that the Norton Electra and early 1960s BMWs could have trouble with, and the bulb wattage is 15–36 watts and the flashing rate 60–120 times per minute.

The speedometer needs to be lit at night, but the instrument is not required on machines first used before October 1937, nor on those under 100 cc and first used before April 1984. The rear number plate just needs to be lit.

Lighting systems

These may be direct or battery, but the first has various technical and legal difficulties. The second is easier to work from as a stable supply line exists to feed all the parts of the system.

The direct system has a definite output and thus must have the correct power bulbs fitted to front and rear lamps. Any marked deviation will have a major effect on the lights, the bulbs and their life.

As all the bulbs are connected at once, it is imperative that the dip switch is of the make-before-break type; otherwise, at that brief instant when the contacts go over, all the power will feed into the rear bulb which will promptly blow. Some protection can be found by using a clipper diode as described later, but the correct switch type will ease the problem.

The need for a stop light is a problem for a machine with direct lighting and there is no easy answer. The system will not be happy if suddenly asked to carry another 21 watts, the normal stop-lamp power, but a solution can be to use a rechargeable cell for the stop light alone. Although not always convenient, it is a solution.

Battery systems do not have this problem but are subject to the limitations of the generator output. This must provide a reserve to ensure some degree of charging for the battery, and the remainder has to balance the load from the head, tail and speedometer lights, the occasional use of the horn and stop light, plus the ignition-system load unless a magneto is fitted.

Any extra load will gradually deplete the battery and thus extra lamps need to be thought about before they are added. If the system is marginal, it may be possible to arrange a series of switches to alternate from one lamp to another, or a pair. Otherwise, the extra lamps should only be used occasionally.

Headlamp

These came in many forms, ranging from a simple shell to a nacelle carrying speedometer, ammeter and switches for lights and ignition. All carry a light unit of some form which may be a sealed beam type or a reflector, glass and bulb. Acetylene types have a burner in place of a bulb and a different manner of construction, but the principle of the reflector is common to all.

Headlamp restoration should be tackled with care and a delicate touch, as many of the detail parts are fragile. Older lamps can have quite a number of parts, especially if a switch or ammeter is built into the rear of them. Any such item should be removed with care and dealt with in its own right.

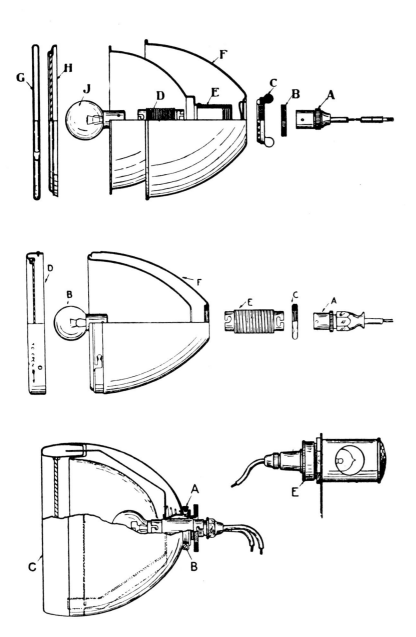

Early Villiers headlamps with various ways of setting the focus and assembling the parts

At the front of the shell goes the rim, glass and reflector assembly which carries the bulb itself. The rim may be held in place with a catch or one or more screws, and its security needs to be checked as the assembly is weighty and fragile. Make sure that the shell is robust enough to support it, bearing in mind that an older one would be in spun brass and itself fragile. It will not like any attempt to alter its shape, being liable to crack. Later ones were in steel and can be refurbished in the same way as other items in that material.

Examine the shell for damage which will need repairing, and look especially for dents to knock out and at the thread in the mountings as this may be very tired. A HeliCoil is one answer where a nut is stripped, and a new turned part for a bolt or stud.

The rim is usually chrome plated and the way it locates to the shell should be examined and repaired as necessary to ensure correct alignment. This is often done with small tabs or local depressions which can easily be distorted so they no longer do their job.

The light unit is held into the rim by a number of wire clips. Four or five are usual but three will do at a pinch, while six is for pessimists. Don't go down to two or the light unit may rattle about in the rim. There should be some form of seal between the two to keep the rain

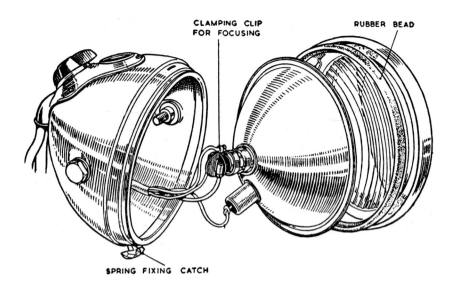

CLAMPING CLIP
FOR FOCUSING

RUBBER BEAD

SPRING FIXING CATCH

Lucas headlamp with
bulb clamp for focusing
and small panel for
switch and ammeter

out and stop the parts damaging one another. Check its condition.

Older light units were assemblies of glass, gasket, reflector and bulb-holder arrangement, all of which could be replaced. The first three were usually glued or clipped together, but in old units the gasket, made from cork, can be expected to have long since crumbled away. It can be replaced with a rubber ring or carefully applied silicon rubber once the two parts are ready for assembly.

The glass began flat and for this type a replacement can usually be contrived by a local glazier. If all else fails, cut a circle out of a pane (bought, not someone's window) and lap a cylinder head in on it to get a diffused light.

Once the glass became domed, replacement became the only answer to a breakage and spares can be hard to find. However, most machines had Lucas lamps in a 6 in. or 8 in. size, and the same glass, clips, bulb holders and reflectors were also used by many cars, which helps the spares situation.

The reflector surface is best left untouched, as even the lightest of dusting can scour the delicate surface. If tarnished, it can be re-silvered, but you may have to search for a company who can handle the job. When it comes back, keep your fingers off !

While early types were brass, silver plated, polished and lacquered, this changed around 1950. The new parts were in steel with a coat of high-glaze enamel to provide the reflecting surface. On to this was deposited aluminium by the vacuum process, which gave a more durable reflector that did not tarnish with age.

They can be re-treated, but, again, you may have to search for a company to handle the work.

The main and pilot bulbs are usually mounted in a single pressing. This locates to the back of the reflector, so the two bulbs fit into holes in the reflector and a wire clip holds the whole assembly in place. The main bulb holder is adjustable, either to one of three positions or by sliding to and fro to give the best light, and then clamping it.

The detail parts are pressings and clips which need to be in good order. The bulb contacts are spring loaded and if worn down can be built up again with solder. The same technique can also revive bulbs if their contact point is worn, and it must be remembered that this is just as much a circuit connection as anything else.

Often the reflector or the bulb holder will have an earth tag or terminal, and this should be exploited for the earth return wire. This, too, is part of the circuit.

Just after World War 2, Lucas had a new light unit with sealed reflector and a pre-focus bulb, which was to come into great favour for motorcycle use. The glass and reflector were sealed together and the glass pattern was on the inside, so the exterior was easy to keep clean.

A pressing in the rear of the reflector provided a housing for the bulb which dropped into place with locations so it was the right way up and correctly positioned for the best focus. A bayonet fixing cap carrying the spring contacts held the bulb in place and provided the

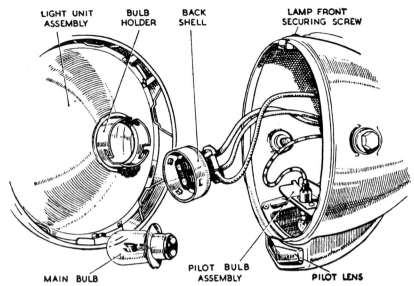

LIGHT UNIT ASSEMBLY — BULB HOLDER — BACK SHELL — LAMP FRONT SECURING SCREW

MAIN BULB — PILOT BULB ASSEMBLY — PILOT LENS

Lucas with pre-focus bulb and underslung pilot lamp

connections, including an earth one. It, too, was designed to fit only in one position and carried a small pilot bulb on its back. This shone through an extra window in the reflector to provide a parking light.

This last feature was initially a problem area, for by 1949 the pilot lamp had become a separate bulb in a housing formed in the underside of the main shell. By 1950 it had assumed a rectangular form but remained of little use when riding. Some firms used twin small lamps as an alternative, with AMC having one on each side of the main shell and Royal Enfield fitting a pair in the corners of its 'casquette', which served the same purpose as a nacelle.

For 1951 the Lucas headlamp gained a block-pattern lens effect for its glass, but otherwise continued as it was. It was available in all kinds of headlamp shells to suit the machines it went on and was often referred to as a 'sealed-beam' lamp. This it was not, as all versions retained the separate bulb and the aperture in the reflector to accept it.

The true sealed-beam lamp is really a large bulb which has the lens formed at the front and the reflector coated at the rear. Three pins at the rear form the connection and it cannot be repaired. It is common on cars but not on motorcycles.

The pre-focus type was revised for 1955 with the pilot bulb in its own little holder in the back

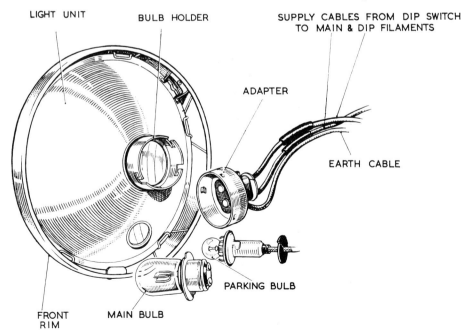

LIGHT UNIT — BULB HOLDER — SUPPLY CABLES FROM DIP SWITCH TO MAIN & DIP FILAMENTS

ADAPTER

EARTH CABLE

PARKING BULB

FRONT RIM — MAIN BULB

The later Lucas pre-focus bulb with pilot lamp set in the reflector, as used by many makes and models

of the reflector. This did away with the under-slung pilot arrangement and in this form the lamp unit ran on for many years. The shells came in various shapes and sizes to suit the machine range, being large or small and either simple or elaborate, but the basic concept remained the same.

This makes replacement easy and also gives the option of using a quartz-halogen bulb, always provided the system can provide the 60 watts of main beam these fire down the road. If you go this route, do not forget that the bulb is small and runs very hot indeed. It must be kept clean and never touched by hand, as the grease and acids will soon ruin it. All come with a means of handling and if touched *must* be cleaned with solvent as instructed.

Stop and tail lamp

Over the years this has grown from a tiny glow-worm into the monsters now used as normal and much needed in modern rush-hour traffic. Early types were made from brass pressings with ruby-red glass lenses, while later ones became steel and plastic with rubber seals.

The brass or steel parts may be repaired and refinished as required and the seals replaced, but the plastic parts can usually only be renewed. Small cracks can be repaired but anything else is too difficult.

The majority of English machines fitted Lucas equipment, and from around 1921, for some three decades, this meant the model MT110: a simple round lamp. In the mid-1930s it was joined by the cheaper MT210 and MT211, both round, and the rectangular ST20 with a stop lamp.

For 1949 there were new round lamps which

shared a common base. These were the 480, which was round with a tubular lens holder, and the 477, with a conical one and thus a larger-diameter lens. Thanks to its increase in size, it could also accommodate a twin-filament bulb for stop and tail lamps. At the same time, AMC adopted the 467/1 which was rectangular with a chrome-plated body, with apertures to rear and down for the plate.

Nearly all makes changed in 1953 when a reflector became a requirement, although at first this was a separate item. The new lamps were the rectangular 525, in diacon plastic, and the oval 529, also plastic, used mainly for light-weights and competition models. At first this was a tail lamp only, but later had a twin-filament bulb fitted.

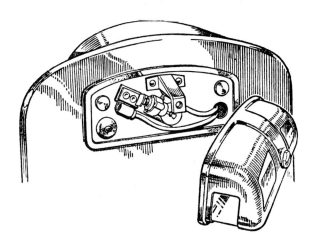

ABOVE **Lucas rear lamp with metal housing, as used by AJS and Matchless for 1949 to 1952**

BELOW **Older Lucas rear lights with MT211 on the left and MT110 to the right**

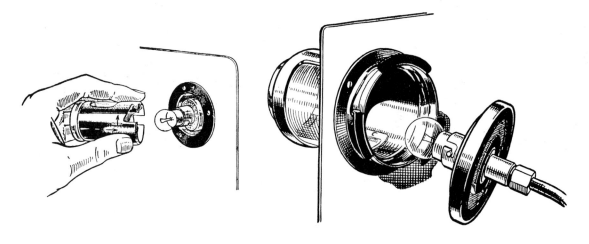

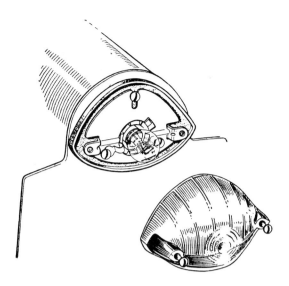

ABOVE Lucas model 529 stop-tail lamp

The 525 was replaced by the 564 in 1955 which had a reflector moulded into the rear lens. It remained in use until the end of the 1960s and went on many machines. At the same time it was joined by the circular L544 for lightweights and the 569 for sidecar use. This last was a front and rear lamp for fixing on the sidecar mudguard. Its moulded body had a front and a rear lens held together by a chrome-plated cover plate.

In 1957, the L590 for lightweights appeared and had a single screw-in bulb and a larger body than the L544. The final lamp was the 679, which came around 1966 and had a rectangular form with an offset round area for the bulb.

There were other makes as well as Lucas, with Miller and Wipac both supplying a variety of rear lamps to manufacturers and the public. They followed the trends in style and the move to plastics for the body. The Miller was listed for a while as the Omnilucent and the original 1955 type was restyled for 1960.

Wipac had a different solution for the stop function and their 1954 lamp had three small bulbs, two being for stop and the centre one for the normal tail. In this way, replacement was cheaper and there was a good chance of at least one bulb remaining in an emergency.

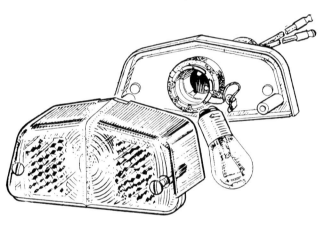

BELOW Lucas model L544 rear lamp

LEFT Lucas model 564 stop-tail lamp with reflector

BELOW Combined front and rear lamps for sidecar use in the Lucas 569 model

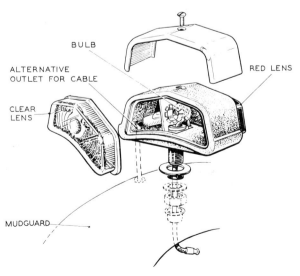

BULB

ALTERNATIVE
OUTLET FOR CABLE

RED LENS

CLEAR
LENS

MUDGUARD

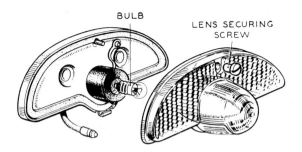

ABOVE Lucas model 590 rear lamp

ABOVE Wipac rear lamp with central tail and two stop bulbs

Clipper diode

The problem of needing the correct dip switch on a direct-lighting system has already been mentioned, but this is compounded by another difficulty. If, or rather when, a headlight filament fails, all the current goes to the tail and speedometer bulbs to blow them as well and give instant, total darkness. Direct lights are also very sensitive to poor earths and bad connections, either of which can cause bulbs to go in disconcerting circumstances.

The answer is the clipper diode, which looks much the same as a zener but is in fact two zener diodes back to back. Its action is to limit, or clip, the positive and negative peaks of the voltage coming from the alternator, thus stabilizing the supply line. Therefore, if the voltage suddenly rises, the diode feeds the excess to ground in the form of heat.

Due to this a heat sink is needed, which can act as the mounting and the earth connection. As always, this is part of the circuit and must make good contact to complete both the electrical and thermal circuits. Be careful when tightening the fixing nut as it is easy to break the copper stud. The other end requires a lead to be soldered to it and this must be done using a small iron, resin-cored solder and a heat shunt to protect the zener diodes from the heat.

The clipper diode should be connected in the feed to the lights after the light switch, so that it only has to work when the lights are on. If connected before, it would have to work all the time. It is only needed to spring into action when the lights are on, and one diode at the right place will protect all the bulbs.

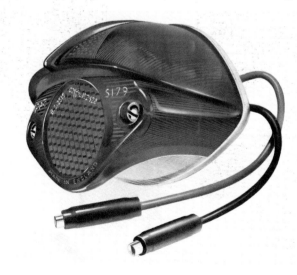

LEFT Wipac S179 rear lamp

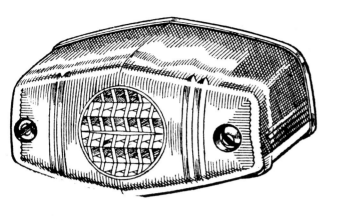

ABOVE **Britax rear lamp with reflector moulded in**

BELOW **The Lucas turn-signal kit with front and rear lamps, flasher unit, switch and warning light**

ABOVE **Heat-sink mounting for a clipper diode**

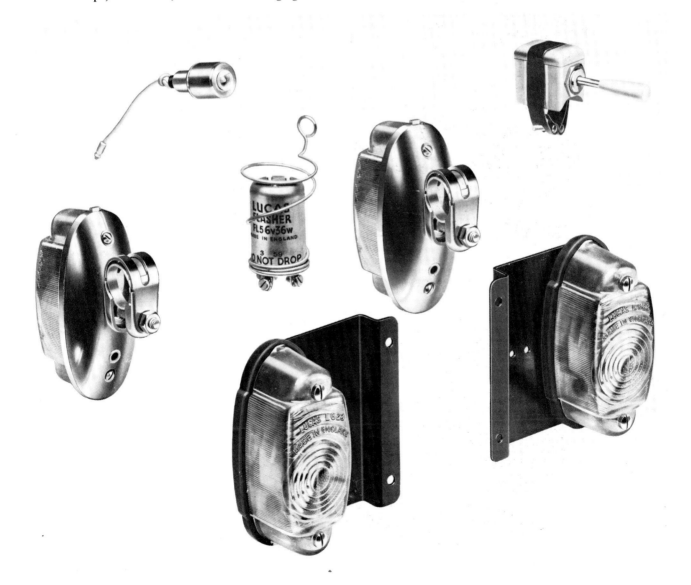

Turn signals

These came to most motorcycles late in the day and so will not appear on many restorations. For those that do use them, the lights can be dealt with in the same way as rear ones, while the flasher unit may be replaced by a modern one if necessary.

It is possible to open up a flasher but it may still refuse to work after your ministrations. Usually, it is easy enough to replace, but check out the connections.

Troubles are more likely to be a refusal to flash, or it will flash at the wrong rate. This can be caused by the now-familiar problems of poor earths, switches and connections. If all is well in this area, look to the bulb ratings, including the warning light, as these have a great bearing on the way the system works.

Ammeter

This was fitted to many machines and either works or does not. It is possible to prise them open but it is tricky work, needing a delicate touch. If it has simply failed it can be retained, after connecting the two wires together, to keep the original appearance, or can be replaced by another of the same size, even if the scale differs. This gradually became less informative as time went on, and progressed from giving a current reading to an unmarked scale with plus or minus.

The ammeter must be connected correctly or it will read in the wrong direction. Reversing the battery connections will have the same effect. Once the latter are correct, simply load the system with the headlight and check that the meter shows a discharge. If it does not, simply reverse the connections.

Owners often wish to add an ammeter to their machine if one is not fitted, which is a simple job provided the machine has battery lighting. If it has direct lighting, or any other form of alternating-current supply, an ammeter cannot be fitted. A mounting will need to be devised to carry the instrument so that it can be seen and its terminals are kept out of the weather.

The wiring needs a little thought, because if the machine has an electric starter, the current for this must not pass through the ammeter as it would ruin it. Also, it is not usual for the horn current to go via the ammeter, so you need to select a point along the line from the battery after the horn supply and before anything else.

Then insert the ammeter into this line. Often this can be done by taking the main battery lead direct to the ammeter and connecting the horn supply to the same terminal. The other terminal is then taken into the lights and ignition switch to provide the power and collect the generator output.

Make quite sure any new wires you add are large enough for the current they will be carrying, which means for most of the system. For the same reason, all terminals must be clean and the connections tight.

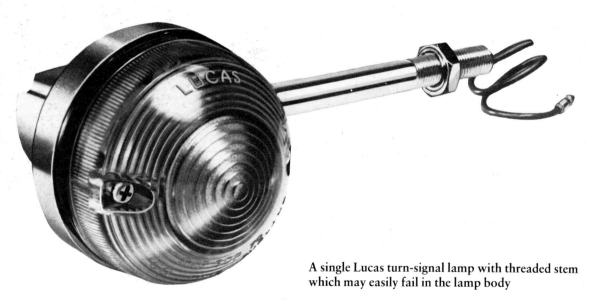

A single Lucas turn-signal lamp with threaded stem which may easily fail in the lamp body

MODEL CZU27
36084F

MODEL CZU27
36088F

MODEL CZU27
36184B

MODEL BM4
36129A E

MODEL BM4
36000A

Horn

Some form of audible warning instrument, as the regulations put it, is required on all machines, and a noisy exhaust will not count! It can be a bulb horn, a mechanical klaxon or, more usually, an electric horn which can be for direct or alternating current. Air horns are added by some owners.

The ac horns rely on the current reversal to pull the diaphragm to and fro, and are mainly found on mopeds and lightweights. They are usually riveted together but can be dismantled and renovated, although in most cases it might be easier just to fit another. Makes consisted of Miller and Wipac, with Lucas joining in for 1957 with their HF 1950. With all these horns, the power is taken direct from the flywheel-magneto lighting coils, so the note varies with the engine speed.

The battery-powered, direct-current horn can usually be dismantled for refurbishing, but note carefully how the parts locate to one another. As the front comes away on most Lucas models, it also has to be moved about to allow the contact points to be disengaged from a slot in the armature.

Check that the coil winding is in order, and if it is not, replace it with one from another unit or try rewinding it. To do this, you will need to measure the diameter of the enamelled copper wire and to count the number of turns needed. Clean up the contact points and all the interior.

ABOVE **A selection of Lucas ammeters with differing scales and background colours**

BELOW **Lucas HF1849 horn, typical of the type**

On assembly, check that the points are closed and that a complete circuit exists through them and the coil from the terminals. Be wary of turning the adjuster too far and keep a note of what you are doing. The centre screw, under the domed nut on Lucas horns, should only just touch or just be clear of the contact blade at rest, and this and any other adjusters need to be set for a good noise at minimum current drain. This will keep contact wear low.

The air horn relies on an electric motor to drive an air pump whose supply is fed to it. Most problems concern connections and the control button, while it is unlikely that repairs to the motor would be practical unless simply to brushes or their wiring.

Due to the current drawn by a horn, and especially by a pair, it is not unusual for a relay to be used to switch them on. This allows the main power lead from the battery to the relay, and then on to the horn, to be short and substantial, while the more remote button on the handlebars only has to switch a small current.

As with so many things electrical, it is the connections, wiring and earths that cause the problems rather than the components. They are the ones to check on first, in all cases.

Section of horn to show the points and adjustments

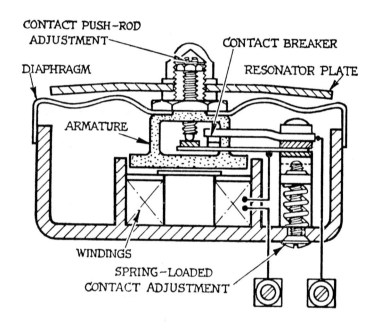

Index

Other motorcycle titles from Osprey

Osprey Collector's Library

AJS and Matchless—The Postwar Models
Roy Bacon   0 85045 536 7

Ariel—The Postwar Models
Roy Bacon   0 85045 537 5

BMW Twins & Singles
Roy Bacon   0 85045 699 1

BSA Gold Star and Other Singles
Roy Bacon   0 85045 447 6

BSA Twins & Triples
Roy Bacon   0 85045 368 2

Classic British Scramblers
Don Morley   0 85045 649 5

Classic British Trials Bikes
Don Morley   0 85045 545 6

Classic British Two-Stroke Trials Bikes
Don Morley   0 85045 745 9

Classic Motorcycle Racer Tests
Alan Cathcart   0 85045 589 8

Ducati Singles
Mick Walker   0 85045 605 3

Ducati Twins
Mick Walker   0 85045 634 7

Continued overleaf

Spanish Trials Bikes
Don Morley   0 85045 663 0

Suzuki Two-Strokes
Roy Bacon   0 85045 588 X

Triumph Twins & Triples
Roy Bacon   0 85045 700 9

Velocette Flat Twins
Roy Bacon   0 85045 632 0

Villiers Singles & Twins
Roy Bacon   0 85045 486 7

Vincent Vee Twins
Roy Harper   0 85045 435 2

Yamaha Dirtbikes
Colin MacKellar   0 85045 660 6

Yamaha Two-Stroke Twins
Colin MacKellar   0 85045 582 0

Osprey Colour Series

Fast Bikes
Colin Schiller   0 85045 761 0

Italian Motorcycles
Tim Parker   0 85045 576 6

Japanese 100hp/11 sec./150 mph Motorcycles
Tim Parker   0 85045 647 9

Road Racers Revealed
Alan Cathcart   0 85045 762 9

Restoration Series

BSA Singles Restoration
Roy Bacon   0 85045 709 2

BSA Twin Restoration
Roy Bacon   0 85045 699 X

Norton Twin Restoration
Roy Bacon   0 85045 708 4

Triumph Twin Restoration
Roy Bacon   0 85045 635 5

General

British Motorcycles of the 1930s
Roy Bacon   0 85045 657 6

British Motorcycles of the 1960s
Roy Bacon   0 85045 785 8

Café Racers
Mike Clay   0 85045 677 0

Ducati Motorcycles
Alan Cathcart   0 85045 510 3

Ducati—The Untold Story
Alan Cathcart   0 85045 789 0

German Post-war Road & Racing Motorcycles
Mick Walker   0 85045 759 9

Honda Gold Wing
Peter Rae   0 85045 567 7

In Pursuit of Perfection
Geoff Duke   0 85045 838 2

Motorcycle Chassis Design: the theory and practice
Tony Foale and Vic Willoughby   0 85045 560 X

Motorcycle Road Racing in the Fifties
Andrew McKinnon   0 85045 405 0

Superbiking
Blackett Ditchburn   0 85045 487 5

The Art & Science of Motor Cycle Road Racing 2nd Editon
Peter Clifford   0 905138 35 X

Track Secrets of Champion Road Racers
Alan Cathcart   0 85045 774 2

Write for free catalogue of motorcycle books to:
The Sales Manager, Osprey Publishing Limited,
27A Floral Street, London WC2E 9DP